1/3/68

THE STARS
TONIGHT

THE STARS
TONIGHT

by John and Cathleen Polgreen

HARPER & ROW, PUBLISHERS
New York, Evanston, and London

ACKNOWLEDGMENTS

Grateful acknowledgment is made to Mount Wilson and Palomar Observatories for the photograph of the Pleiades and Nebulosity in Taurus, copyright by California Institute of Technology and Carnegie Institution of Washington, which appears on the jacket and cover of this book. All photographs in the book are from the Mount Wilson and Palomar Observatories with the exception of the central region of Orion on page 17 and the upper photograph of Coma Berenices on page 39, which are by the authors.

The authors wish to express particular thanks to James S. Pickering, Astronomer Emeritus of the Hayden Planetarium, for his assistance in the preparation of this book.

THE STARS
TONIGHT

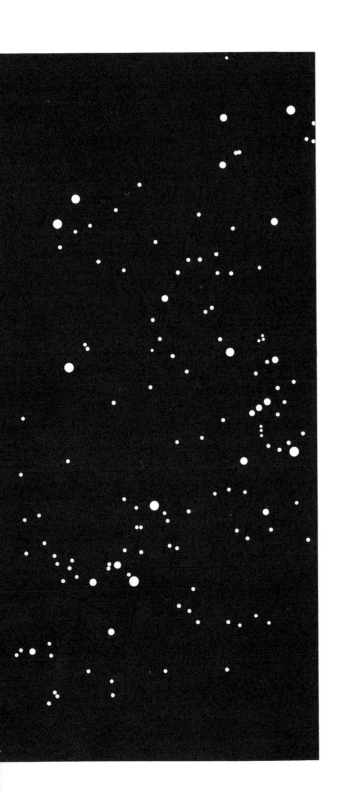

THE STARS
TONIGHT

On a clear night, when there is little moonlight, you can look deep into space. What you see at first may appear to be only a jumble of stars, as confusing as the ones on the chart to your left, which represents a small part of the sky. Long ago man looked at the same sky we see and tried to create some order out of the confusion by naming groups of stars, or constellations, after various figures from mythology. It is by many of the same names that we identify the constellations we see today.

2

The chart on this page is the same as the one on the left, except that lines have been added to connect the main stars in each constellation. Later on, with a little imagination, you will be able to picture some of the mythological figures the constellations were supposed to represent. We will mention briefly a few of the legends told about them, which are entertaining and sometimes helpful. Associating a group of stars with a certain shape or story makes the constellation easy to locate and remember.

Now we have a "road map" of this part of the sky, but it is not yet complete. To make it useful, we need to find out where, how, and when to look for these stars.

3

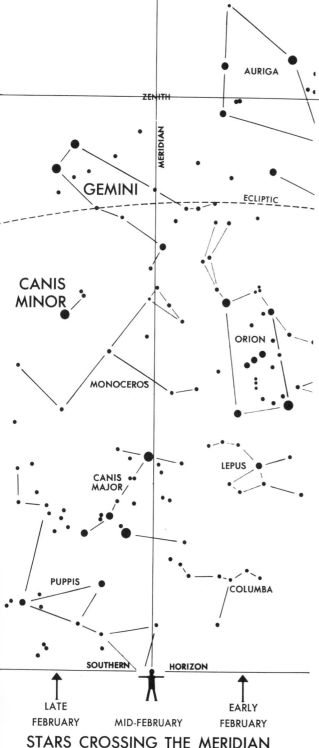

DIRECTION OF STARS' MOTION

AURIGA

ZENITH

MERIDIAN

GEMINI

ECLIPTIC

CANIS MINOR

ORION

MONOCEROS

LEPUS

CANIS MAJOR

PUPPIS

COLUMBA

SOUTHERN   HORIZON

LATE FEBRUARY   MID-FEBRUARY   EARLY FEBRUARY

STARS CROSSING THE MERIDIAN

FEBRUARY—FACE SOUTH
9:00 P.M. STANDARD TIME

Here is the same chart that we saw on the previous page. It now shows black stars on a white background to make it more clearly visible when you take the book out-of-doors. The chart shows the stars that you will see as you face south at about nine o'clock at night in the middle of February. Similarly, each month is represented by charts which show what you can see by looking north or south at any time of year. If the sky is clear, you can take the book with you to watch the stars, tonight or any night.

Looking South

You may need a pocket compass to find north and south from the point where you intend to watch the stars. Or you can find these directions in the time-honored way—by using the Big Dipper as a guide. To see how this is done, turn to page nine to the section on the north celestial pole.

From an area with the clearest view of the sky, face directly south and look

4

straight ahead. Disregard trees, buildings, mountains, and other obstructions that may limit part of your view. Just imagine that you are looking right through them. What you are locating is a point in space. Whether you are at ground level or on a high building, when you look straight ahead, you are looking toward the *horizon*. This is marked on the chart by the head of the little figure.

The Zenith

Slowly raise your head straight up until you are looking at the point in the sky that is directly overhead. This point is called the *zenith* and is marked near the top of each chart.

The Meridian

Your eyes have just traced an imaginary line in the sky, from the southern horizon to the zenith. This line is part of the *meridian* and is marked by the center line on the chart. The meridian passes directly over your head from north to south, through the zenith.

As you face south, the constellations on or near the meridian are at their highest point in the sky and in the best position for viewing. These are the ones we will explore each month. With a little practice in looking from horizon to zenith, you will find it very easy to locate the stars you have seen on the charts in their positions in the sky.

Direction of Stars' Motion

As the earth makes its annual journey around the sun, we are able to see different stars at different times of the year. The earth is also turning on its axis as it travels around the sun. Because of this axial motion, the stars which we see while facing south appear to rise in the east, move across the sky, and set in the west.

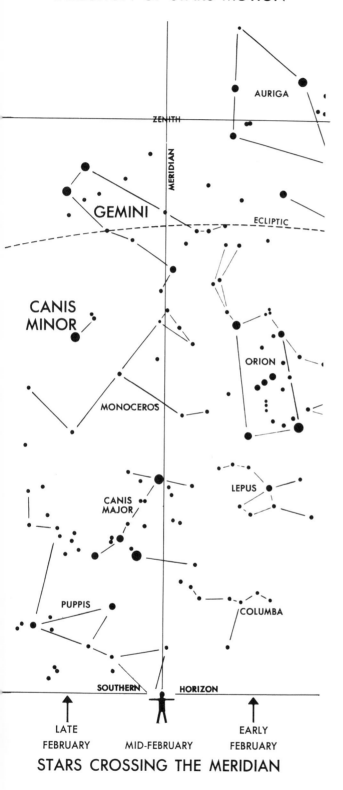

STARS CROSSING THE MERIDIAN

FEBRUARY—FACE SOUTH
9:00 P.M. STANDARD TIME

The Ecliptic and the Zodiac

The sun also appears to rise and set because of the turning of the earth. The path that the sun seems to follow across the sky is called the *ecliptic* and is marked on the chart with a dotted line. The ecliptic is also the center of the path that the moon and planets appear to follow across the sky. These paths almost coincide because the planets travel around the sun in orbits which are in nearly the same plane as the orbit of the earth.

An imaginary belt which includes that part of the sky slightly above and below the ecliptic is called the *zodiac*. In ancient times it was divided into twelve parts. The constellation that lies within each of these areas is called a *zodiacal constellation*, one of which will be explored each month.

Occasionally you will see a bright clear "star" along the zodiac that does not appear on the chart. Chances are that this will be a planet.

The Month and the Hour

Open the book to the present month. The key chart shows the stars as they appear on the meridian at about 9:00

6

P.M. Standard Time, or 10:00 P.M. Daylight Saving Time. It also shows which stars will be on the meridian early and late in the month.

It is a good idea at first to get your bearings at this time of night. On a clear night you may occasionally want to watch the sky at a later hour. Or on the long winter nights you might want to go outdoors early. Until you are acquainted with the stars and their east to west motion, you will find the table on pages 82 and 83 a convenient guide to the correct chart for use during the early or late hours.

Where Are You?

The charts have been worked out for the central latitude of the United States. If you live in the extreme north, your southern horizon and zenith will be a little higher than shown. Your northern horizon will be a little lower. If you live in the extreme south, the exact opposite will be true. In either case the change is slight.

The charts have also been plotted for the central area of the time zones. If you are located near the edge of a time zone, the stars may be slightly farther to the east or west of the meridian than they appear to be on the charts.

The Expanded Charts

Any constellation labeled with large letters on the key chart to the left is shown in an expanded view to the right, allowing you to study the constellation in detail. The dotted lines, except for the ecliptic lines, indicate the boundaries of surrounding constellations. The close-up views include *more stars than you can normally see* with the unaided eye, unless the conditions for viewing are ideal. The size of all the stars is greatly exaggerated for easy visibility. If you squint at the charts under a light, you will see the stars more nearly as they appear in the sky. Any star or phenomenon mentioned in the text is labeled in a chart on the same or facing page.

Looking North

The final chart for each month shows the northern constellations. On page 8 we have a view of the February sky. Except for the position of the stars, the FACE

7

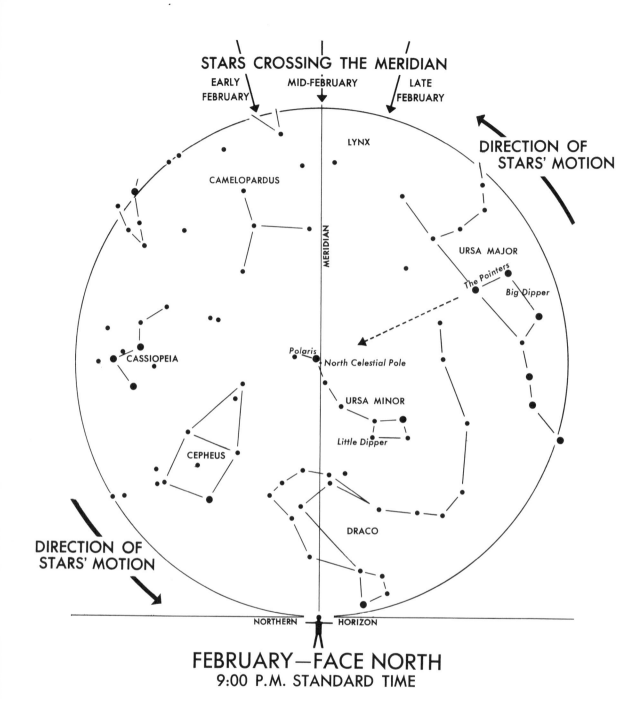

STARS CROSSING THE MERIDIAN

EARLY
FEBRUARY

MID-FEBRUARY

LATE
FEBRUARY

LYNX

DIRECTION OF
STARS' MOTION

CAMELOPARDUS

MERIDIAN

URSA MAJOR

The Pointers

Big Dipper

CASSIOPEIA

Polaris

North Celestial Pole

URSA MINOR

Little Dipper

CEPHEUS

DIRECTION OF
STARS' MOTION

DRACO

NORTHERN   HORIZON

FEBRUARY—FACE NORTH
9:00 P.M. STANDARD TIME

NORTH charts will be the same throughout the book. As you look at the northern horizon, marked by the head of the little figure, trace an imaginary line from that point to the zenith (directly overhead). This line is a continuation of the meridian, marked on the chart by the center line. The zenith is slightly above this line. It is not shown because the stars at the zenith and a bit beyond appear on the FACE

8

SOUTH charts and are *not* seen all year round. From central latitudes in the United States, the stars on these northern charts *are* visible all year. We will review them as they take turns climbing high on the meridian.

The North Celestial Pole

Polaris is the star that marks, or nearly marks, the north celestial pole. This is a point in space directly above the earth's north pole. As the earth turns, the other stars seem to circle around Polaris like the rim of a wheel revolving around its hub.

Locating Polaris will always help you find your position. Use the Big Dipper as a guide. The Dipper is a large bright figure that is easily found whether it is high or low in the sky. On any night of the year two stars of the Dipper, called the Pointers, lead straight to Polaris, as you can see on the chart. When you face Polaris you are facing north. Directly behind you is south. East is to your right, and west to your left.

What Will You See?

Given a clear night you will, of course, see the constellation patterns. But once you are familiar with a constellation, there are often many things to look for within its boundaries. We will point out some of the finest objects for viewing—to name a few: stars of all colors, double stars, clusters of stars, variable stars, and occasionally the misty glow of a far-off nebula or galaxy.

The glossary beginning on page 85 will clarify any unfamiliar terms, and you may want to glance at it in advance.

Night Vision

A fact that cannot be overemphasized is that it takes time for your eyes to become adapted to the dark after leaving a lighted room. As your "night eyes" become adjusted there will be a tremendous increase in the number of stars you can see.

You will probably want to use this book out-of-doors, and to preserve your night vision, only a dim light should be used. A flashlight covered with tissue paper, held with a rubber band, provides a good diffused light. A red tissue cover is even better.

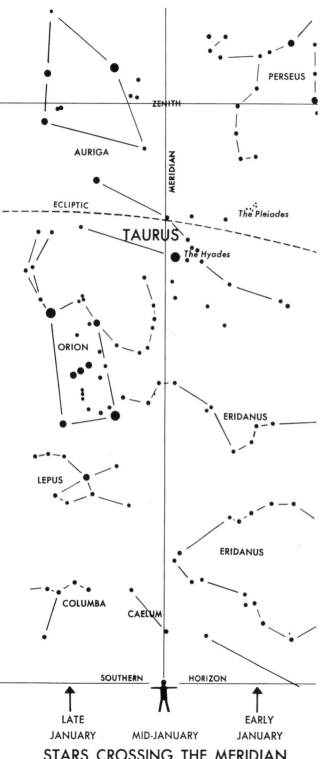

PERSEUS

ZENITH

AURIGA

MERIDIAN

ECLIPTIC

The Pleiades

TAURUS

The Hyades

ORION

ERIDANUS

LEPUS

ERIDANUS

COLUMBA

CAELUM

SOUTHERN HORIZON

LATE JANUARY   MID-JANUARY   EARLY JANUARY

STARS CROSSING THE MERIDIAN

JANUARY—FACE SOUTH
9:00 P.M. STANDARD TIME

JANUARY

Four of the brightest stars in the heavens will cross your meridian this month. The first one is in the zodiacal constellation of Taurus, the Bull, high in the sky on the ecliptic. A bright V-shaped cluster of stars marks Taurus' face. This cluster is called the Hyades (hi' a deez) and from it glares the bull's eye—a bright reddish star named Aldebaran (al deb' a ran).

Another fine cluster of stars, which marks the bull's shoulder, is called the Pleiades (plee' a deez), or the Seven Sisters. Most people can count four or five stars easily, and it is possible that the legendary lost sisters were once bright stars that grew dim. If you can count more than six stars, your eyesight is excellent. Through binoculars you can see many more in this area. It has been discovered that this whole group of stars is surrounded by a nebulosity, or cloudy appearance, which can be partially detected in the telescopic photograph on the opposite page.

Near the tip of the bull's lower horn is M1, the Crab Nebula. This is the

10

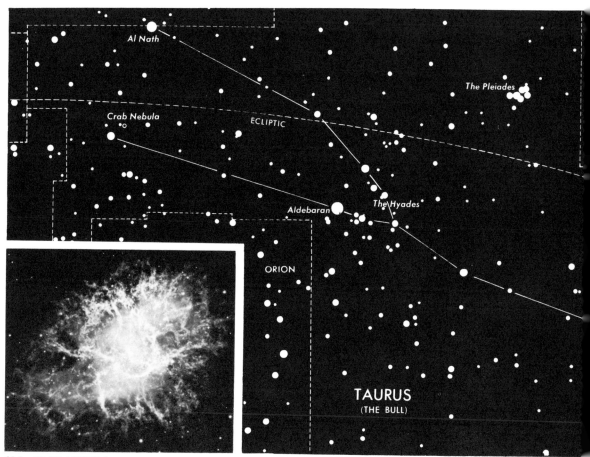

M 1 CRAB NEBULA

nebula that the French astronomer Charles Messier used to begin his famous catalog of over one hundred interesting objects in the sky. They are known as M, or Messier, objects. Although not visible to the unaided eye, the Crab Nebula, in the photograph above, is unique in appearance. It is thought to be the remains of a star that exploded in the year 1054, leaving a bright gaseous cloud to mark the cataclysm.

THE PLEIADES

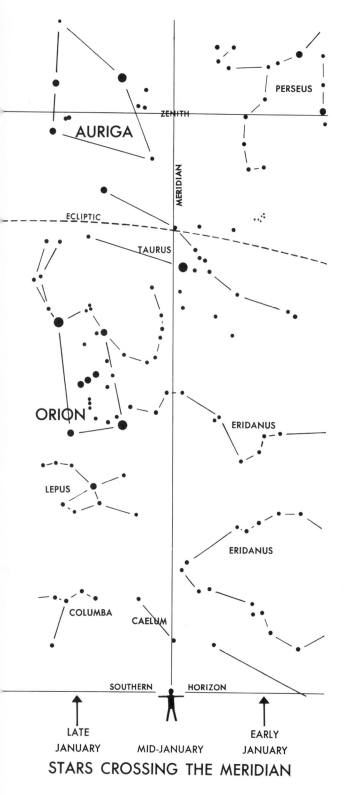

DIRECTION OF STARS' MOTION

PERSEUS

ZENITH

AURIGA

MERIDIAN

ECLIPTIC

TAURUS

ORION

ERIDANUS

LEPUS

ERIDANUS

COLUMBA

CAELUM

SOUTHERN   HORIZON

LATE
JANUARY   MID-JANUARY   EARLY
JANUARY

STARS CROSSING THE MERIDIAN

JANUARY—FACE SOUTH
9:00 P.M. STANDARD TIME

Al Nath marks the tip of Taurus' upper horn. Above it is the constellation Auriga, the Charioteer, which is directly overhead after mid-January. Auriga is a clear, kite-shaped figure that can be found easily by locating the golden star Capella. This is the third brightest star that can be seen from our latitudes.

One legend claims that Auriga, because he was lame, invented the horse-drawn chariot. But he was also associated with shepherds and is usually pictured carrying a goat in one arm. The goat is represented by Capella, and the pretty little triangle of stars beneath it is called the Kids, or little goats. In ancient times there were good stars and bad stars, and the Kids had the reputation of being "horrid mad stars." Because they always appeared in the sky during the stormy season, it was thought that they must be to blame for the weather.

If you have binoculars, the whole area inside the quadrangle of Auriga is an excellent hunting ground for some beautiful star clusters and double stars.

The impressive figure of Orion (o ri´ on), the Hunter, is at its highest point in the sky at the end of the month. Because of Orion's brilliant geometric pattern, he dominates the winter sky and is probably the easiest of all the

12

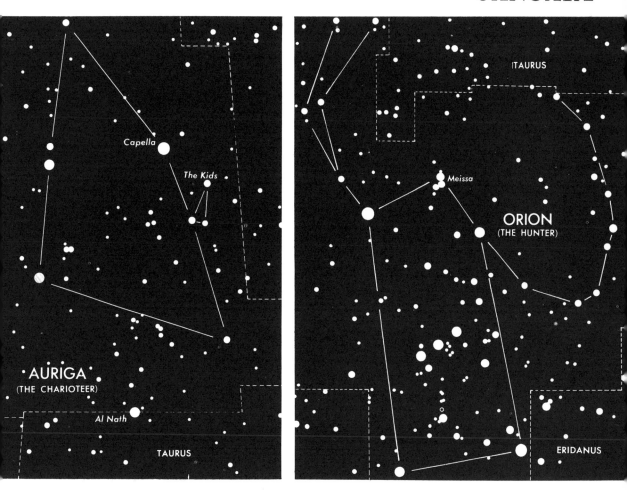

constellations to find. There are so many exciting things to see in Orion that you can spend many nights exploring it. For a beginning, look at the mythical figure itself.

Legends portray Orion as a magnificent giant, and it is not difficult to see why. Four of the brightest stars form a rectangle which represents the body of the hunter. Within the rectangle are three more bright stars in a straight row—Orion's belt. Dropping from the belt is what looks like a string of little stars that decorate his sword. One of these "stars" is M42, which we'll look at later. To the right of the rectangle is a loop of stars—a lion's skin draped over one arm. Rising from the left is a dim starry arm brandishing a club in the endless pursuit of Taurus, the Bull, who is just out of reach. Centered above the rectangle is a small triangle of stars called Meissa, which means "the head of the giant."

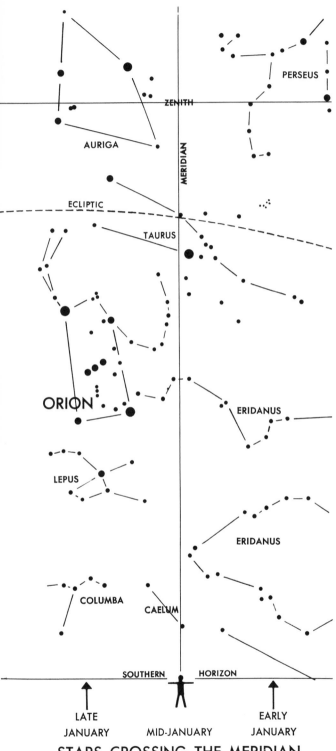

DIRECTION OF STARS' MOTION

ZENITH

MERIDIAN

PERSEUS

AURIGA

ECLIPTIC

TAURUS

ORION

ERIDANUS

LEPUS

ERIDANUS

COLUMBA

CAELUM

SOUTHERN HORIZON

LATE JANUARY

MID-JANUARY

EARLY JANUARY

STARS CROSSING THE MERIDIAN

JANUARY.—FACE SOUTH
9:00 P.M. STANDARD TIME

The red star named Betelgeuse (bet′ el jooz), marking Orion's shoulder, was the first to be measured by a remarkable instrument called an interferometer. It was found to be an enormous, pulsating, variable star. If it were in the position of our sun, its diameter would reach well outside the orbits of the earth and Mars.

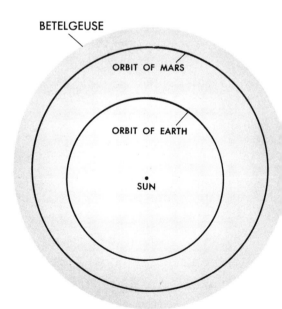

BETELGEUSE

ORBIT OF MARS

ORBIT OF EARTH

SUN

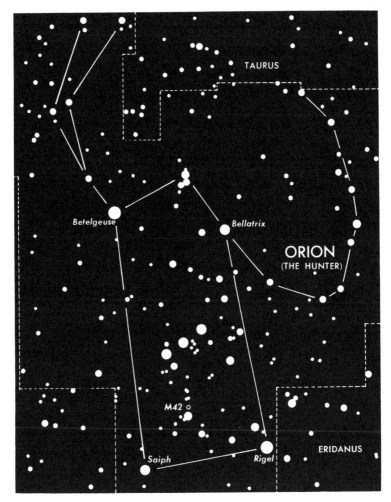

Rigel (rye' jel) is the brilliant white star in Orion diagonally opposite Betelgeuse. Although its distance from us is over twice that of Betelgeuse, it is still the seventh brightest star in the sky. Actually, it is about 25,000 times brighter than our sun. Rigel is a double star; through a small telescope a faint blue companion can be seen. It is interesting to compare Rigel with the red Betelgeuse to sharpen your awareness of star colors.

As the Orion rectangle is such a landmark of the winter sky, it is worthwhile to know the names of the other two stars. The yellow one at the upper right corner is Bellatrix, named in honor of Orion's mother. The star opposite Rigel is called Saiph.

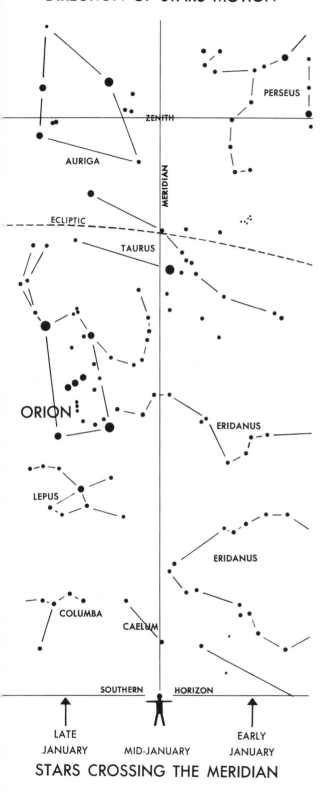

DIRECTION OF STARS' MOTION

ZENITH

PERSEUS

AURIGA

MERIDIAN

ECLIPTIC

TAURUS

ORION

ERIDANUS

LEPUS

ERIDANUS

COLUMBA

CAELUM

SOUTHERN | HORIZON

LATE JANUARY

MID-JANUARY

EARLY JANUARY

STARS CROSSING THE MERIDIAN

JANUARY—FACE SOUTH
9:00 P.M. STANDARD TIME

The photograph at the top of the opposite page shows the area of Orion's belt and sword, which contains two very impressive nebulae. Look carefully at the center "star" in the sword, and you will see that it is not a star at all but a small misty spot. This is the Great Nebula, also called M42. It is one of the few nebulae that can be seen clearly without optics. But if an instrument is available, by all means turn it toward M42. It is impressive through binoculars, and through a telescope it is one of the loveliest sights in the sky. It appears as a shimmering green mist, roughly fan-shaped and sprinkled with faint stars.

The other nebula is just south of the lowest star in the belt and is called the Horsehead, or Dark Bay, Nebula. It cannot be seen without optics, but a powerful telescope shows it as a clear black silhouette against a luminous background, as seen in the bottom photograph. If you turn the picture upside

16

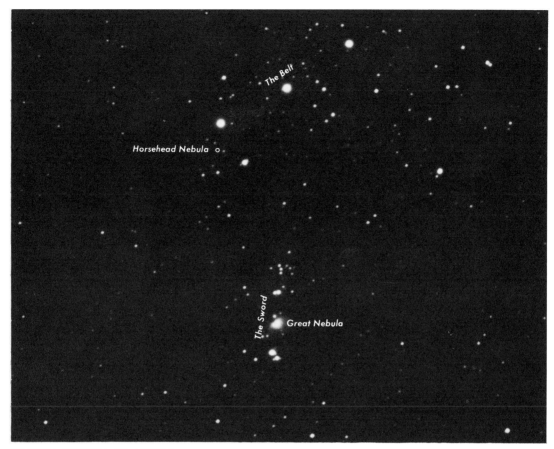

The Belt

Horsehead Nebula o

The Sword

Great Nebula

CENTRAL REGION OF ORION

GREAT NEBULA

HORSEHEAD NEBULA

down, you will see the horse's head and neck quite clearly. For many years this region was believed to be a "hole in the sky" where there were no stars. The dark nebula is made of dust and gas which block off the light of the stars.

Eridanus (e rid′ an us), the River, is a rather faint but easily traced pattern of stars. It covers a large area of the sky as it follows a winding route to the south. Marking the end is a brilliant

17

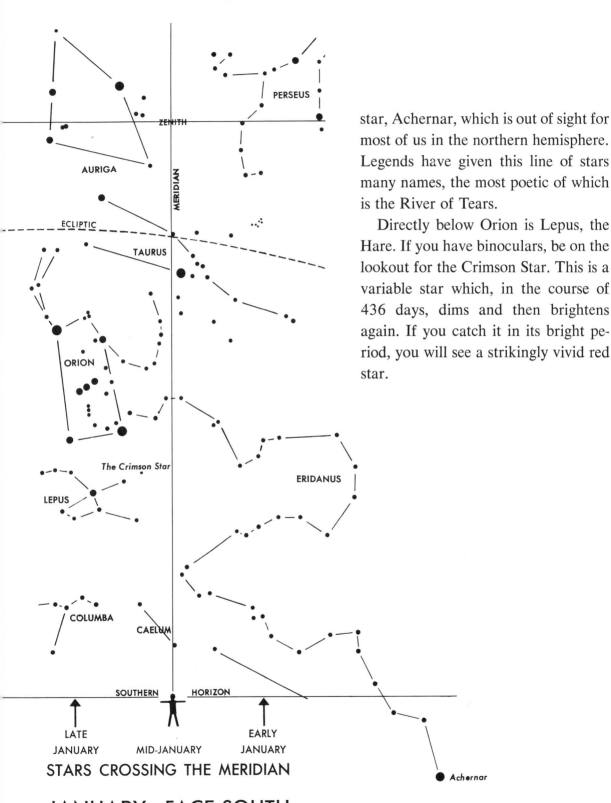

DIRECTION OF STARS' MOTION

PERSEUS

ZENITH

AURIGA

MERIDIAN

ECLIPTIC

TAURUS

ORION

The Crimson Star

ERIDANUS

LEPUS

COLUMBA

CAELUM

SOUTHERN   HORIZON

LATE
JANUARY

MID-JANUARY

EARLY
JANUARY

Achernar

STARS CROSSING THE MERIDIAN

JANUARY—FACE SOUTH
9:00 P.M. STANDARD TIME

star, Achernar, which is out of sight for most of us in the northern hemisphere. Legends have given this line of stars many names, the most poetic of which is the River of Tears.

Directly below Orion is Lepus, the Hare. If you have binoculars, be on the lookout for the Crimson Star. This is a variable star which, in the course of 436 days, dims and then brightens again. If you catch it in its bright period, you will see a strikingly vivid red star.

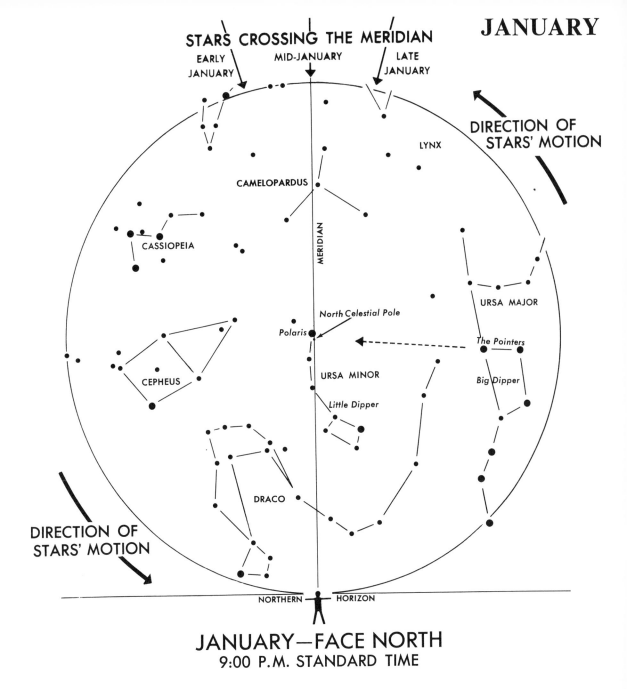

STARS CROSSING THE MERIDIAN

JANUARY

EARLY JANUARY · MID-JANUARY · LATE JANUARY

DIRECTION OF STARS' MOTION

LYNX

CAMELOPARDUS

CASSIOPEIA

MERIDIAN

North Celestial Pole

Polaris

URSA MAJOR

The Pointers

CEPHEUS

URSA MINOR

Big Dipper

Little Dipper

DRACO

DIRECTION OF STARS' MOTION

NORTHERN — HORIZON

JANUARY—FACE NORTH
9:00 P.M. STANDARD TIME

As though subdued by the wonderful view to the south, the upper part of the meridian to the north doesn't offer much of interest this month. The only constellation crossing it is Camelopardus, a very faint figure which is, incidentally, not a camel but a giraffe.

The Big Dipper is on an "uphill" climb over the northeast horizon.

19

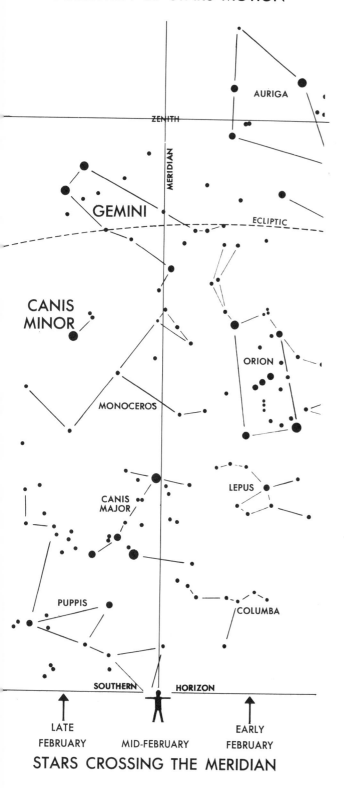

STARS CROSSING THE MERIDIAN

FEBRUARY—FACE SOUTH
9:00 P.M. STANDARD TIME

FEBRUARY

This is another excellent month for star hunters. You can still enjoy January's spectacular sights a little to the west while more stars come into their best positions for viewing. The zodiacal figure of Gemini, the Twins, will be on the ecliptic high in the sky. First find the two bright stars which mark the twins' heads. Extending from these will be seen two roughly parallel lines of stars that complete the major part of the figure.

From earliest times this constellation has represented twins, probably because of the closeness and brightness of its two main stars, Castor and Pollux. Castor is a beautiful double star, though it can be seen as a double only with a telescope. It is greenish-white, whereas Pollux is somewhat brighter and yellow in color.

20

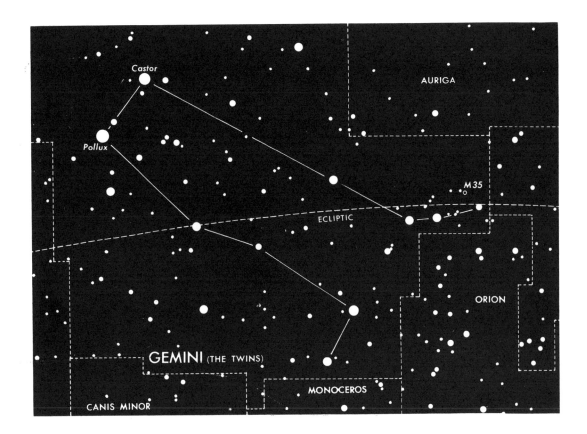

Above the feet of Gemini is M35, a faint, hazy patch on the clearest of nights. Binoculars will transform it into a lovely cluster of stars.

Directly south of Pollux is another brilliant yellow star named Procyon (pro′ see on), found in the constellation of Canis Minor, the Little Dog. In legends the dog has had many masters, but because he follows Orion so faithfully across the sky, he is generally conceded to be the hunter's dog.

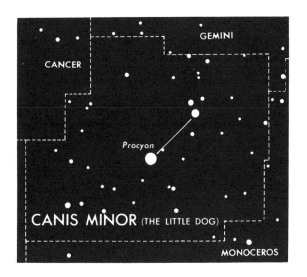

21

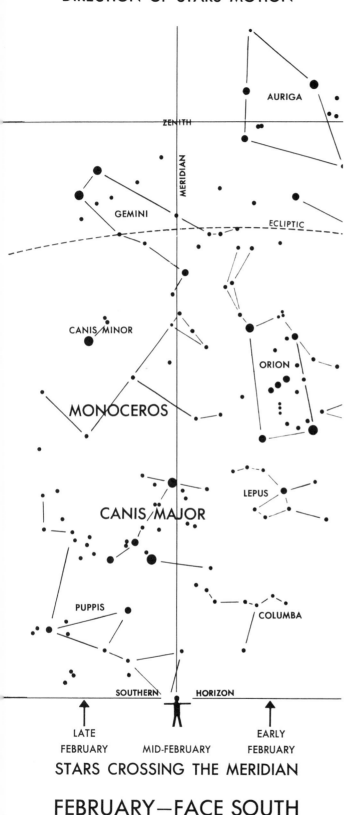

STARS CROSSING THE MERIDIAN

FEBRUARY—FACE SOUTH
9:00 P.M. STANDARD TIME

The brightest star in the sky is the blue-white Sirius, located in Canis Major, the Big Dog. The brilliant appearance is due more to the relative closeness of Sirius to the earth than to the actual brightness of the star.

The ancient Greeks feared the fiery Dog Star. They thought that it was in league with the sun and responsible for intense heat, dried-up crops, mad dogs, and various illnesses. On the other hand, the ancient Egyptians held this beautiful star in reverence, and with good reason. For the people along the Nile, its appearance in the early morning sky of late summer heralded the approaching time when the river would overflow its banks and flood the parched valley. After the yearly flood subsided, crops would flourish and the people would prosper.

Look for M41, a lovely star cluster in Canis Major, with a red star near its center.

Between Canis Major and Canis Minor is Monoceros (mo no' se ros), the Unicorn—not a very exciting constellation but a good test of your ability to find stars. On a clear night see if you can distinguish a nice open cluster designated as NGC 2244 on the chart.

22

In Monoceros is found a rare phenomenon, which can be observed only with a powerful telescope. Variable stars are fairly common, but here we find a *variable nebula*. Its light seems to pulsate at rapid intervals, as a result of one or more variable stars being embedded in the nebula.

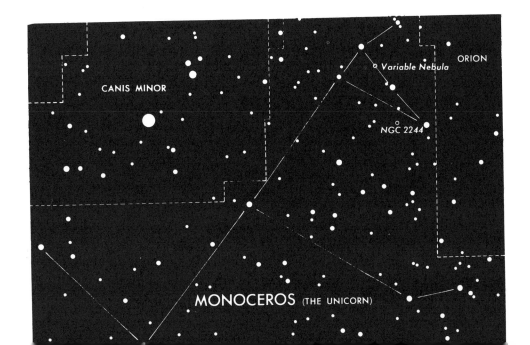

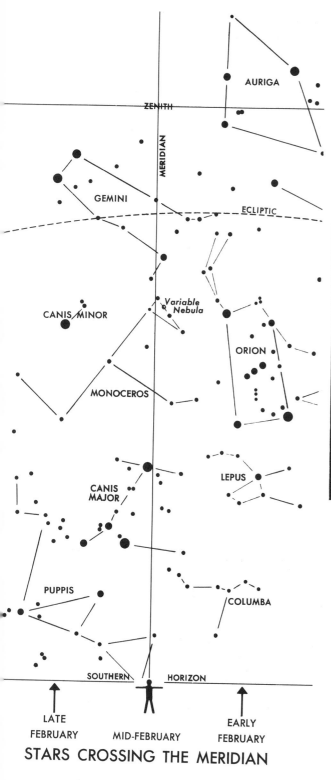

DIRECTION OF STARS' MOTION

AURIGA

ZENITH

MERIDIAN

GEMINI

ECLIPTIC

CANIS MINOR

Variable Nebula

ORION

MONOCEROS

CANIS MAJOR

LEPUS

PUPPIS

COLUMBA

SOUTHERN   HORIZON

LATE FEBRUARY

MID-FEBRUARY

EARLY FEBRUARY

STARS CROSSING THE MERIDIAN

FEBRUARY—FACE SOUTH
9:00 P.M. STANDARD TIME

HUBBLE'S VARIABLE NEBULA

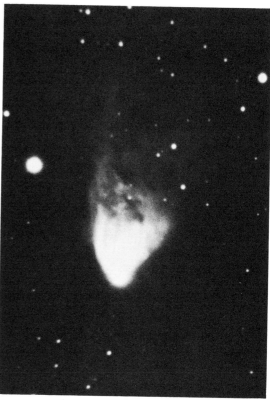

Sometimes called Hubble's Variable Nebula in honor of its discoverer, it has the distinction of being the subject of the first photograph, shown above, ever taken with the 200-inch Hale telescope.

Just above the southern horizon is Columba, the Dove, and Puppis, the Stern, which is mentioned again in March.

24

FEBRUARY

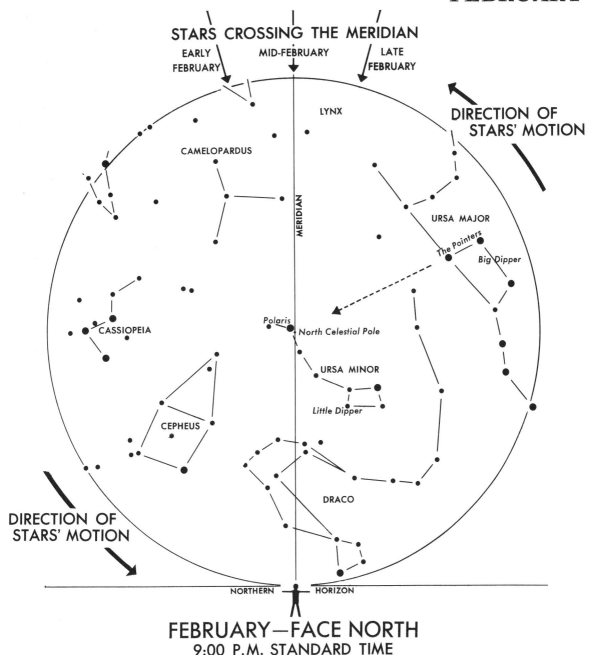

STARS CROSSING THE MERIDIAN

EARLY FEBRUARY   MID-FEBRUARY   LATE FEBRUARY

LYNX

CAMELOPARDUS

DIRECTION OF STARS' MOTION

MERIDIAN

URSA MAJOR

The Pointers

Big Dipper

CASSIOPEIA

Polaris

North Celestial Pole

URSA MINOR

Little Dipper

CEPHEUS

DIRECTION OF STARS' MOTION

DRACO

NORTHERN HORIZON

FEBRUARY—FACE NORTH
9:00 P.M. STANDARD TIME

Overhead are some of the inconspicuous stars of Lynx, so named because only a person with acute eyesight, or "lynx eyes," can see it.

With the Big Dipper to the east and Cassiopeia to the west, all of the bright constellations are concentrated in the bottom part of the northern circle. The sky above Polaris seems rather bleak.

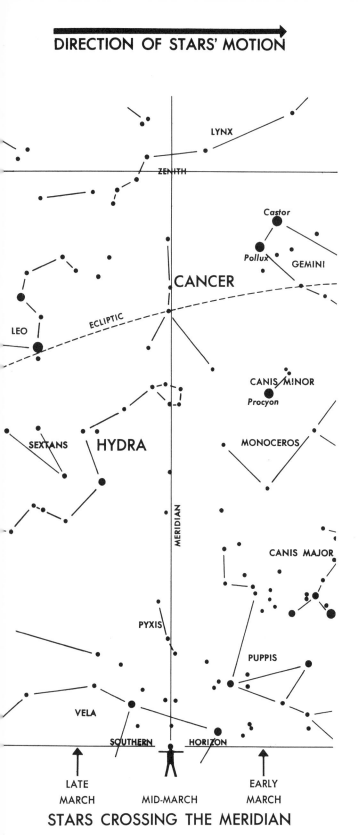

DIRECTION OF STARS' MOTION

LYNX

ZENITH

Castor

Pollux

GEMINI

CANCER

ECLIPTIC

LEO

CANIS MINOR
Procyon

SEXTANS   HYDRA

MONOCEROS

MERIDIAN

CANIS MAJOR

PYXIS

PUPPIS

VELA

SOUTHERN   HORIZON

LATE
MARCH   MID-MARCH   EARLY
MARCH

STARS CROSSING THE MERIDIAN

MARCH—FACE SOUTH
9:00 P.M. STANDARD TIME

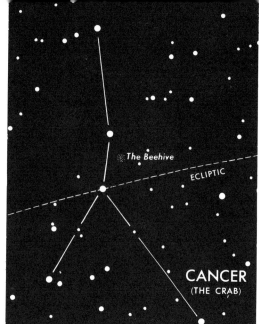

The Beehive

ECLIPTIC

CANCER
(THE CRAB)

MARCH

The stars crossing the meridian in March seem dim compared to those of other months. You will probably prefer looking to the west to catch sight of some of the brighter figures of February.

However, this month you will want to locate Cancer, the Crab, an inconspicuous zodiacal constellation on the ecliptic, shaped like an upside-down Y. In mythology Cancer was linked with Hercules, the heroic giant of the July sky. It seems that the crab was sent to destroy the giant by biting his toes, a unique method of combat. Fortunately he didn't succeed, and Hercules stays well out of Cancer's way in the sky.

Wait for a clear moonless night and use some of the brighter stars such as Castor, Pollux, or Procyon as guides to this faint constellation. When you have

26

the figure carefully in view, you will see a spot of light forming a narrow triangle with two of Cancer's main stars. This is M44, or Praesepe (pree see′ pay). The popular name for Praesepe is the Beehive. Long ago it was mistaken for a nebula or a comet until Galileo turned his small, newly invented telescope toward it. With binoculars you can share the joy that he felt when he resolved it into separate stars. You will see a lovely open star cluster suggesting a glittering hive of bees. While Galileo counted about forty stars, today's large telescopes have recorded around four hundred.

A little loop of stars just south of Cancer represents the head of Hydra, the Sea Serpent. This is the longest constellation in the sky and will be on our charts for the next two months. Despite its large size, there is only one bright star in Hydra. This red star has been well-named Alphard, which means "the Solitary One."

Down on the southern horizon are some figures that were once part of the great constellation Argo Navis, the Ship of the Argonauts. Because of its tremendous size and as a convenience to astronomers, Argo was later divided into four separate constellations. Given a good southern view, you can see Puppis, the Stern, Pyxis, the Compass, and part of Vela, the Sails. Out of sight for most of us is Carina, the Keel.

At the top of the chart is part of the constellation called Lynx. This figure is also mentioned in February, but it contains very little of interest in either month.

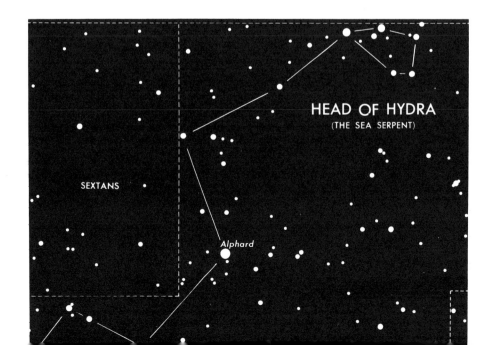

HEAD OF HYDRA
(THE SEA SERPENT)

SEXTANS

Alphard

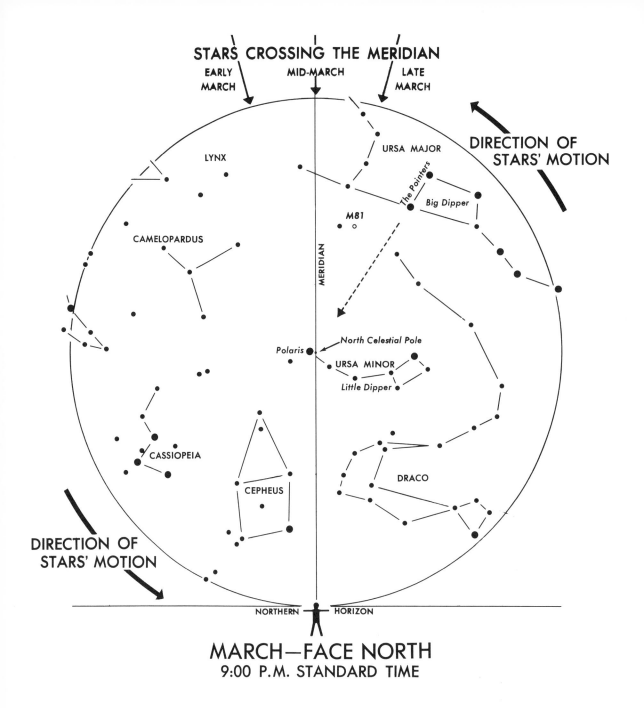

STARS CROSSING THE MERIDIAN

EARLY MARCH · MID-MARCH · LATE MARCH

DIRECTION OF STARS' MOTION

LYNX

URSA MAJOR

The Pointers

Big Dipper

M81

CAMELOPARDUS

MERIDIAN

North Celestial Pole

Polaris

URSA MINOR

Little Dipper

CASSIOPEIA

CEPHEUS

DRACO

DIRECTION OF STARS' MOTION

NORTHERN — HORIZON

MARCH—FACE NORTH
9:00 P.M. STANDARD TIME

The head and front paws of Ursa Major, the Great Bear, start across the meridian late in March, to be followed in coming months by the most familiar part of the figure, known as the Big Dipper. At this point the bear is high in the sky, and you will have to picture him as being upside down if indeed you can picture him at all. This brings up a puzzling question. How did this group of stars having no resemblance to a bear happen to be named the Great Bear by the North American Indians as well as by ancient civilizations across the Atlantic?

One possible explanation is that bears were known to inhabit the colder northern lands of both civilizations, and it was natural for the people to look northward toward the "land of the bears" and name the most impressive of the northern constellations for these great beasts. At any rate, we know the Great Bear was the subject of entertaining stories on both continents. We will talk about some of the tales in May when more of the constellation is overhead.

Some magnificent galaxies and nebulae are located in Ursa Major, but a telescope is needed to see them. This photograph shows three in one field, the brightest of which is the dazzling spiral galaxy M81.

M81 AND NEIGHBORING GALAXIES

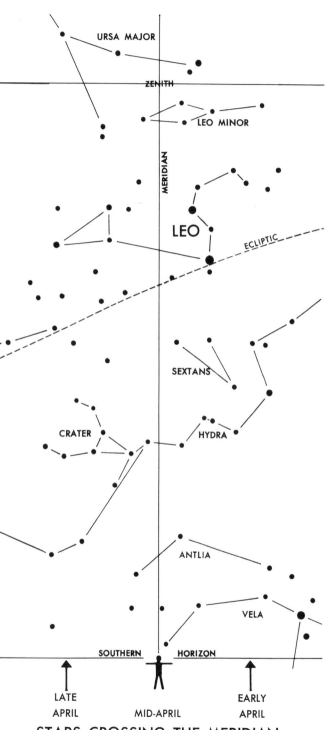

URSA MAJOR

ZENITH

LEO MINOR

MERIDIAN

LEO

ECLIPTIC

SEXTANS

CRATER

HYDRA

ANTLIA

VELA

SOUTHERN   HORIZON

LATE
APRIL

MID-APRIL

EARLY
APRIL

STARS CROSSING THE MERIDIAN

APRIL—FACE SOUTH
9:00 P.M. STANDARD TIME
10:00 P.M. DAYLIGHT SAVING TIME

APRIL

The king of the April sky is Leo, the Lion, the zodiacal figure on the ecliptic, whose appearance is a welcome herald of summer. This is an easy constellation to recognize because of its two well-defined patterns. The sickle shape marks Leo's great shaggy head, and at the bottom of the sickle the bright star Regulus marks his heart. The rest of the lion is represented by a triangle with a fairly bright star, Denebola, at the outermost angle. Leo seems to recline in the sky like a stately well-fed cat.

Early Egyptians associated Leo with the Sphinx. But in Greek legend he was usually pictured as a less docile beast. He was supposed to have been the ferocious lion who terrorized the population of a peaceful valley. Hercules, the Giant, whom we will see in July, was given the job of killing Leo, whose coat

30

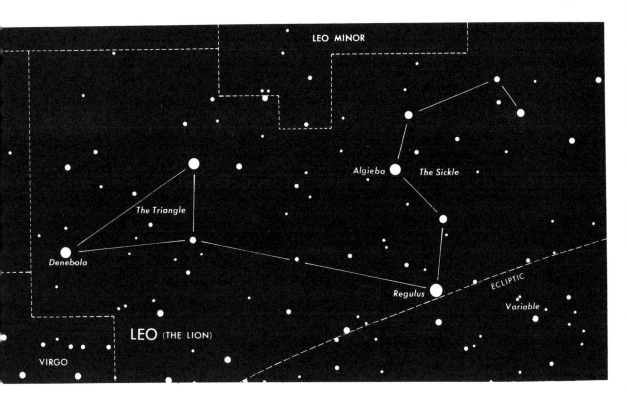

no arrow could penetrate. The brave giant subdued the lion with his bare hands and thereafter wore the lion's skin.

There are some good double stars in this area, many of which require optics if their components are to be separated. This is the case with Regulus, a white star with a faint, and very close, blue companion. The second bright star above Regulus in the sickle is Algieba, a binary system. It is a beautiful yellow star with a green companion, said to be the finest double visible from the northern latitudes. A 3-inch telescope is needed to split it.

A little to the west of Regulus is a well-known red variable star (the lower star of the pair marked on the chart). At its brightest it can be seen without optics, and then it slowly dims beyond visibility. It makes one complete cycle, from bright to dim to bright, every 313 days.

Some wonderful galaxies and nebulae are within Leo's boundaries. They are too splendid to be ignored even though we cannot see them without a telescope.

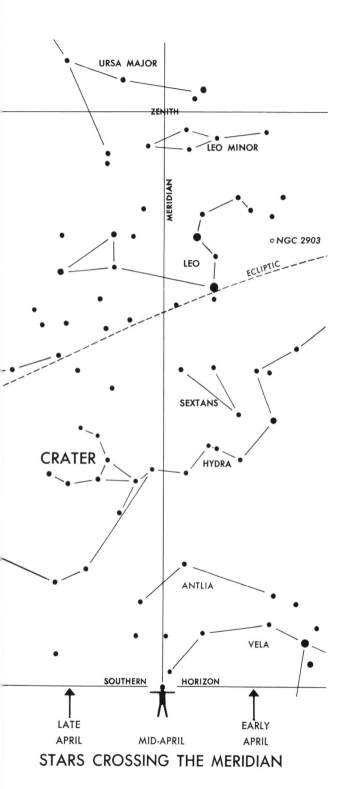

STARS CROSSING THE MERIDIAN

APRIL—FACE SOUTH
9:00 P.M. STANDARD TIME
10:00 P.M. DAYLIGHT SAVING TIME

The one pictured opposite is the spiral galaxy NGC 2903, located off the blade end of the sickle.

Above Leo, almost overhead, is Leo Minor, a delicate diamond-shaped figure with nothing very exciting to offer the viewer. Some of the lesser stars of Ursa Major, the Great Bear, also appear at the top of the chart, but we will investigate this constellation when we face north.

The stars of Hydra, the Sea Serpent, continue to wind across the meridian toward the south. Hydra's head appears on the March charts, and his tail will continue through May. Seemingly resting on the monster's back is the pretty little constellation known as Crater, the Cup. This is a rather lonely section of the sky, and Crater is quite faint. But on a good clear night you can easily make out the base and the half circle of stars that look very much like a tilted goblet.

Most of the constellations seen from northern latitudes have suitably dramatic names. But the ancient people who named the star groups and wove legends around them lived north of

32

NGC 2903

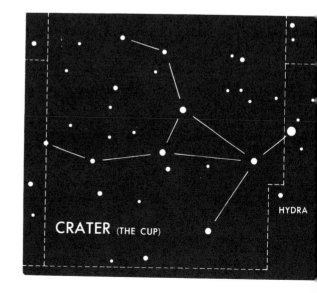

CRATER (THE CUP)

HYDRA

the equator. The extreme southern constellations were out of sight and unknown to them. Not until the early sixteenth century, when Magellan made his voyage around the tip of South America, did the southern stars become important to navigators and explorers. This accounts for the prosaic, modern names of most of these constellations. For example, consider the little group of stars located just southwest of Crater. It is called Antlia, the Air Pump.

33

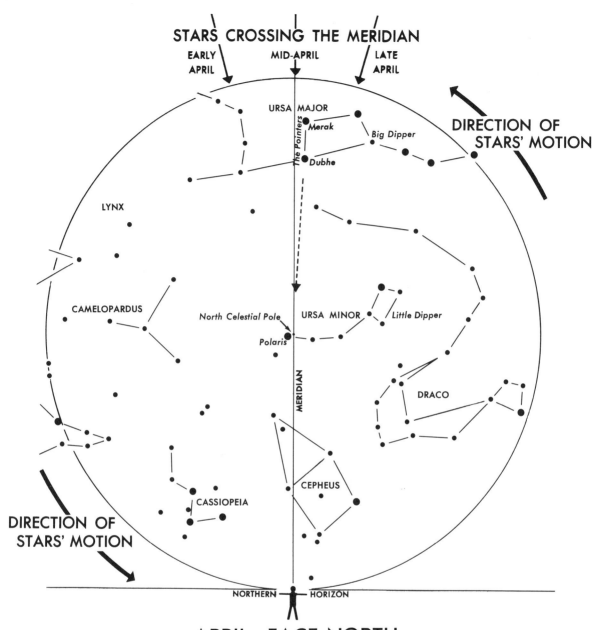

STARS CROSSING THE MERIDIAN

EARLY APRIL   MID-APRIL   LATE APRIL

DIRECTION OF STARS' MOTION

URSA MAJOR

Merak

Big Dipper

The Pointers

Dubhe

LYNX

CAMELOPARDUS

North Celestial Pole

URSA MINOR   Little Dipper

Polaris

MERIDIAN

DRACO

DIRECTION OF STARS' MOTION

CEPHEUS

CASSIOPEIA

NORTHERN HORIZON

APRIL—FACE NORTH
9:00 P.M. STANDARD TIME
10:00 P.M. DAYLIGHT SAVING TIME

At about mid-April, the most familiar part of Ursa Major, the Great Bear, begins to climb overhead. This is the Big Dipper, probably the most universally recognized group of stars in the sky. It is big and bright and can be seen all year-round by those with a good view to the north.

34

We will explore the whole Dipper in May, but this month we can concentrate on two of its most important stars, which have the Arabic names of Dubhe and Merak. They are better known as the Pointers and will lead you to the North Star, or Polaris. Extend a line about five times the distance between these two stars. Near the end of this line you will see only one fairly bright star—Polaris. This is an important one to know because it is very close to the north celestial pole. Polaris seems to stay in one place while the other stars appear to move around it like a giant wheel turning around a fixed center. Thus the term *circumpolar* (around the pole) is used for the stars on the northern charts.

The drawing below shows what happens when a camera is aimed at Polaris and set for a time exposure. Each semicircular line is the path of a star. But this path is not caused by star motion; it is caused by the turning of the earth. The center path is that of Polaris which, as you can see, remains almost in the same spot. Find Polaris and you will have a celestial compass. No matter where you are, when you face this star, you are facing north. South is behind you, east to your right, and west to your left.

STAR TRAILS AROUND
THE POLE

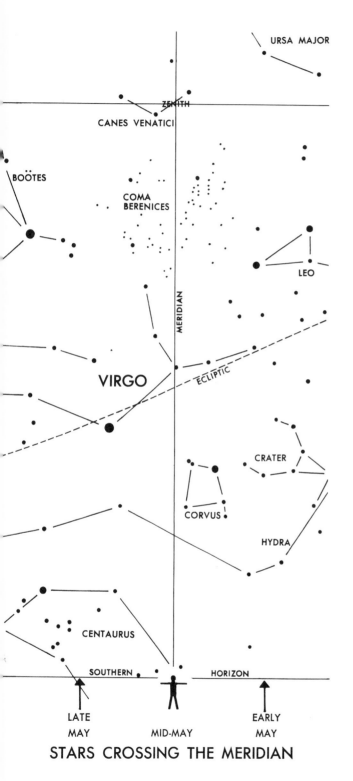

URSA MAJOR

ZENITH

CANES VENATICI

BOÖTES

COMA
BERENICES

MERIDIAN

LEO

VIRGO

ECLIPTIC

CRATER

CORVUS

HYDRA

CENTAURUS

SOUTHERN

HORIZON

LATE
MAY

MID-MAY

EARLY
MAY

STARS CROSSING THE MERIDIAN

MAY—FACE SOUTH
9:00 P.M. STANDARD TIME
10:00 P.M. DAYLIGHT SAVING TIME

MAY

The best way to get your bearings this month is to find Spica (spy′ka), a sparkling white star in the zodiacal figure of Virgo, the Virgin, on the ecliptic. Spica will cross the meridian, a little less than halfway up from the horizon, toward the end of the month. Earlier in the month look for it slightly east of the meridian. Above and to the right of Spica are five paler stars arranged in a large open V, completing the most interesting part of the figure.

According to one legend, Virgo was the Goddess of Justice and Purity. She fled to the sky when mankind proved to be cruel and wicked. The ancients had no means of seeing the fantastic treasures that Virgo guards. But today, with a good-sized telescope or with photographs taken by the world's largest instruments, we can look deep into the sky at some of her wonders. However, before we go treasure hunting, there is one more stop to·make.

36

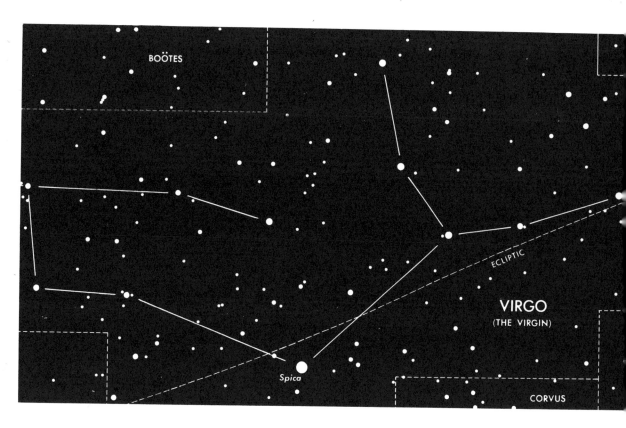

Look at the area filled with stars above the arm of Virgo in a constellation with a charming name—Coma Berenices, or Berenice's Hair. Try to find this one after you have been outdoors for some time and your "night eyes" are sharp. You will see an open cluster of stars, so elusive that they seem to flicker on and off like fireflies. Binoculars will transform this area into a clear and almost unbelievably rich field for viewing.

A cluster of stars, such as we see in this constellation, can be taken in stride. The hazy patch of a far-off galaxy like our own seems awesome, but acceptable. Now imagine, if you can, a *cluster of galaxies*. These clusters are the telescopic treasures found in the area around Coma Berenices, and extending down through the constellation of Virgo.

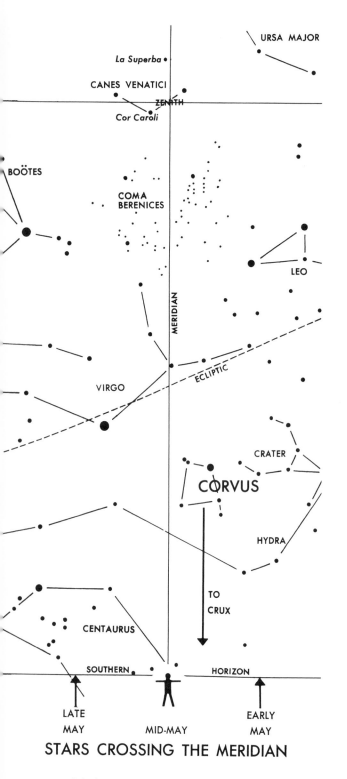

URSA MAJOR

La Superba •

CANES VENATICI

ZENITH

Cor Caroli

BOÖTES

COMA
BERENICES

LEO

MERIDIAN

VIRGO

ECLIPTIC

CRATER

CORVUS

HYDRA

TO
CRUX

CENTAURUS

SOUTHERN

HORIZON

LATE
MAY

MID-MAY

EARLY
MAY

STARS CROSSING THE MERIDIAN

MAY—FACE SOUTH
9:00 P.M. STANDARD TIME
10:00 P.M. DAYLIGHT SAVING TIME

A comparison of photographs, on the right, shows what an ordinary camera and a giant telescopic camera can record. The top picture was taken in the authors' backyard and shows a large part of the field where the galaxy clusters are found. Although this time exposure brings up many more stars than the eye alone can see, it lacks the great magnification needed to capture the galaxies. The photograph below it was taken with the 200-inch Hale telescope and shows a cluster of galaxies in just one small section of Coma.

The galaxies become even more numerous in the Virgo cluster—there are thousands known to be in this area.

The small constellation of Canes Venatici, the Hunting Dogs, is right on the zenith. There is no mythology attached to the dogs as they were not named until the seventeenth century. At that time they were pictured on a leash in the hand of the Herdsman, whom we will meet in June. Again, telescopic galaxies are abundant in the area in and around Canes Venatici, where there are two particularly notable stars.

38

COMA BERENICES

CLUSTER OF GALAXIES IN COMA BERENICES

The brightest star in Canes is Cor Caroli, meaning Charles' Heart. It was named in memory of King Charles I of England and is one of the few "modern" stars to be named after a prominent person. This is quite a nice double star and can sometimes be separated with binoculars.

Look for the star on the chart with the modest name of La Superba. It is a variable star with a period of 158 days, and hardly superb in size. But when you catch it at or near its maximum brightness, you will see that it is a brilliant red star.

Down toward the horizon, old friend Hydra, the Sea Serpent, is still working his way across the meridian. He appears on the March and April charts, but this month we can officially say good-bye to all but the tip of his tail.

The little quadrangle of stars above Hydra is Corvus, the Crow. Corvus makes a good pointer to the sparkling constellation of Crux, the famous Southern Cross. Crux is out of sight from all but the extreme southern parts of the United States.

Although Centaurus is visible now, this constellation will be mentioned in June when it can be seen more easily.

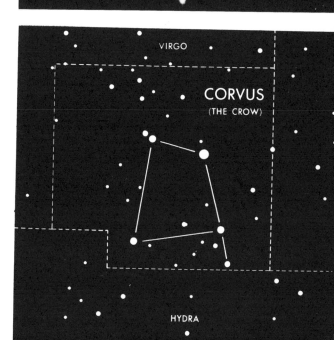

VIRGO

CORVUS
(THE CROW)

HYDRA

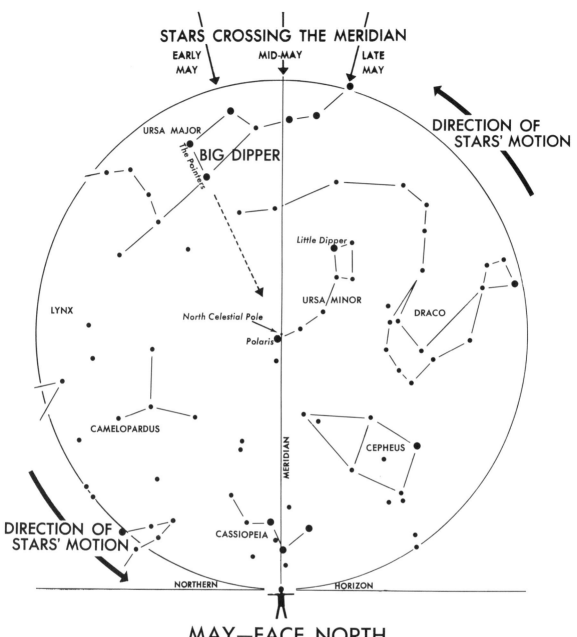

STARS CROSSING THE MERIDIAN

EARLY MAY   MID-MAY   LATE MAY

DIRECTION OF STARS' MOTION

URSA MAJOR

The Pointers

BIG DIPPER

Little Dipper

URSA MINOR

DRACO

LYNX

North Celestial Pole

Polaris

CAMELOPARDUS

CEPHEUS

MERIDIAN

DIRECTION OF STARS' MOTION

CASSIOPEIA

NORTHERN   HORIZON

MAY—FACE NORTH
9:00 P.M. STANDARD TIME
10:00 P.M. DAYLIGHT SAVING TIME

March and April saw some of the stars in Ursa Major, the Great Bear, cross the meridian. Now the most prominent part of this constellation, the Big Dipper, will hang high overhead, dominating the northern sky. The four stars of the bowl and the three bright stars of the handle stand out in a brilliant pattern. You can add a little glamor to these stars by knowing their Arabic names, which are given in the chart opposite. These are shortened versions of the original long Arabic phrases and do not always agree with those used on other charts. For instance, Benetnasch is sometimes called Alkaid, and Phad is also known as Phecda.

Concentrate on Mizar, the middle star in the handle, and you will see a tiny star, Alcor, right next to it. This pair is usually called the Horse and Rider or, in England, Jack-on-the-Middle-Horse.

In April we talked about finding Polaris by using the Pointers as a guide. In March it was noted that civilizations separated by an ocean saw Ursa Major as a bear, which seems hard to explain. Some of the stories from both continents are quite delightful and deserve to be touched on briefly.

Observers of the stars in ancient times endowed our bear with a glorious bushy tail (the handle of the Dipper). Perhaps the chart makers had never seen a bear and did not realize that he has almost no tail. Nevertheless, one story has it that the Great Bear constantly travels around the pole, hoping to capture Polaris and add it to his fine bejeweled tail.

The North American Indians, who knew a bear when they saw one, realistically left off his tail and used the bowl of the Dipper to represent the bear. What they did with the tail, however, took some wild imagination. One legend turns these three stars into a hunting party sent to chase the bear around the pole. And a fearsome group of hunters they were. The first hunter, the robin, was armed with a bow and arrow for killing the bear. The second warrior (Mizar) was the chicka-dee who carried a little pot (Alcor) to cook him in. The last one was the moosebird who was in charge of carrying the sticks for the fire. Each fall they wounded the bear, and his blood turned the autumn leaves to red. But the old bear always recovered and, to this day, manages to keep ahead of the hunters as the chase goes on and on. Fortunately they have never had to face the problem of how to fit the big bear into the tiny pot.

There is only one obstruction between the Dipper bowl and Polaris. This is the tail of Draco, the Dragon, whom we will see more of in the next few months.

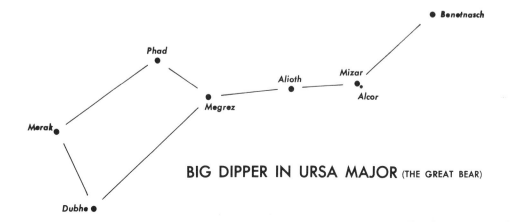

BIG DIPPER IN URSA MAJOR (THE GREAT BEAR)

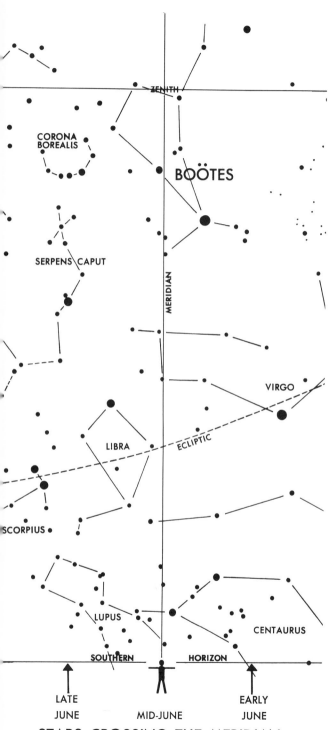

STARS CROSSING THE MERIDIAN

JUNE—FACE SOUTH
9:00 P.M. STANDARD TIME
10:00 P.M. DAYLIGHT SAVING TIME

JUNE

The sky in summer is a delight to any stargazer watching the parade of fascinating figures that move steadily across the meridian.

The first of the big summer constellations is Boötes (boh oh′ tez), the Herdsman. He is high in the sky, a long kite-shaped figure punctuated by a huge golden-orange star, Arcturus. The three stars forming a roof shape at the top of the "kite" represent his head and shoulders. His arm seems to be reaching for the Big Dipper in the northern sky.

Depending on which legend one wants to accept, Boötes can be doing a variety of heavenly chores. He is credited with inventing the plow (which the Dipper is sometimes called), attaching it to two oxen, and driving it across the sky. Or he may, like Atlas, be reaching toward the pole in an effort to hold up

42

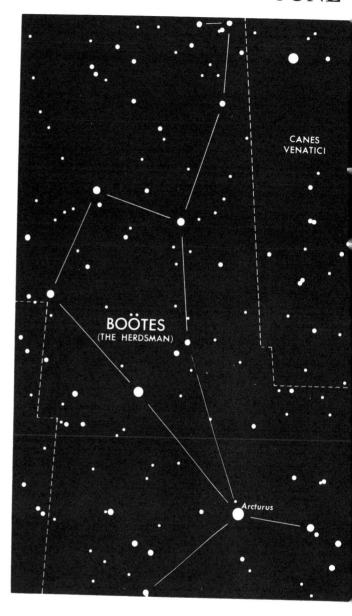

the heavens. Or Boötes and his hunting dogs, Canes Venatici, may be on a bear hunt for Ursa Major in the north.

Arcturus, the brightest star in the area of Boötes, was instrumental in an important discovery about the nature of the universe. Until about 250 years ago it was believed that the stars were in absolutely fixed positions, and their only motion was caused by the turning of the earth. But when Arcturus and some other prominent stars were compared with a 2000-year-old catalog, it was found that they had moved away from their former recorded positions. This discovery led to further research, and it is now known that none of the stars is stationary. Some are moving at a rate of several hundred miles per second. Despite the great speed of these "runaway stars," distances in space are so vast that the movement is not noticeable. In fact, the change of a star's position could not be detected by the human eye in a lifetime.

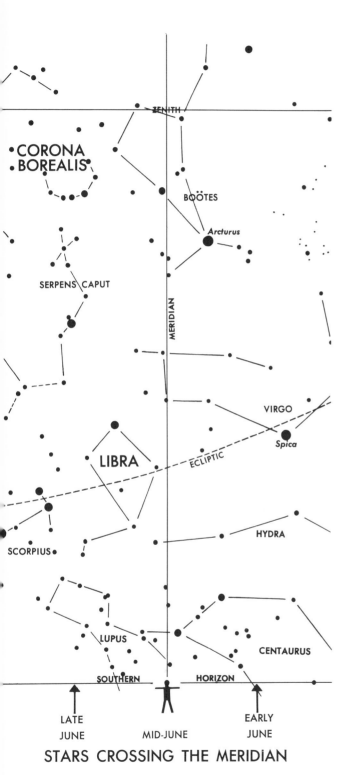

DIRECTION OF STARS' MOTION

CORONA
BOREALIS

BOÖTES

Arcturus

ZENITH

SERPENS CAPUT

MERIDIAN

VIRGO

Spica

LIBRA

ECLIPTIC

HYDRA

SCORPIUS

LUPUS

CENTAURUS

SOUTHERN HORIZON

LATE
JUNE

MID-JUNE

EARLY
JUNE

STARS CROSSING THE MERIDIAN

JUNE—FACE SOUTH
9:00 P.M. STANDARD TIME
10:00 P.M. DAYLIGHT SAVING TIME

East of Boötes' shoulder is a fragile semicircle of seven stars forming the lovely Corona Borealis, the Northern Crown. Its one bright star, Gemma, is called the Pearl of the Crown. There is a variable star marked on the chart which is highly irregular. For long periods, sometimes years, it will be just visible to the unaided eye on a clear night. It will then, unpredictably, fade out of sight in a matter of weeks.

Look for the attractive double star to the northeast of Corona. Both stars are yellow and well separated.

Corona is often called Ariadne's Crown, the wedding crown of the beautiful princess Ariadne of Greek legend. It has also been pictured by American Indians as a circle of warriors around a campfire.

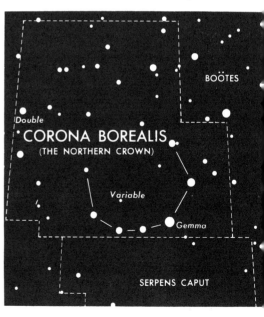

Double

CORONA BOREALIS
(THE NORTHERN CROWN)

BOÖTES

Variable

Gemma

SERPENS CAPUT

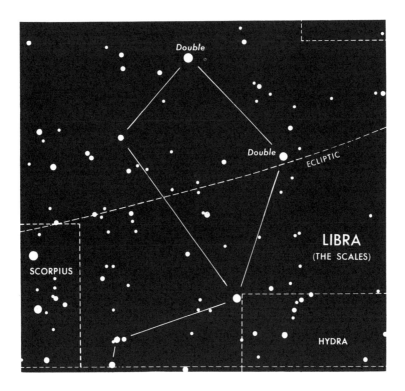

Directly below Corona is part of Serpens, the Serpent, which we will see more of in July. This section of the figure is called Serpens Caput (cap′ ut), which means "the Serpent's Head."

Southwest of Arcturus you can easily find the bright star Spica, which will help in completing the dim pattern of Virgo seen on the May charts. Next to Virgo on the ecliptic, is the zodiacal figure of Libra, the Scales, perhaps the scales on which Virgo, the legendary Goddess of Justice, weighed the fate of mortals. The star at the top of the quadrangle is a most unusual pale green color. Both this and the other star marked on the chart, are good double stars to separate with binoculars.

Down on the southern horizon is the top part of Centaurus, the Centaur, a figure that is half man and half horse. This constellation is notable for its brilliant multiple star, Alpha Centauri, which is out of sight in these latitudes. Alpha Centauri is the nearest star to us beyond the sun—near being *270,000 times the distance between the earth and the sun.*

Lupus, the Wolf, is also seen near the horizon.

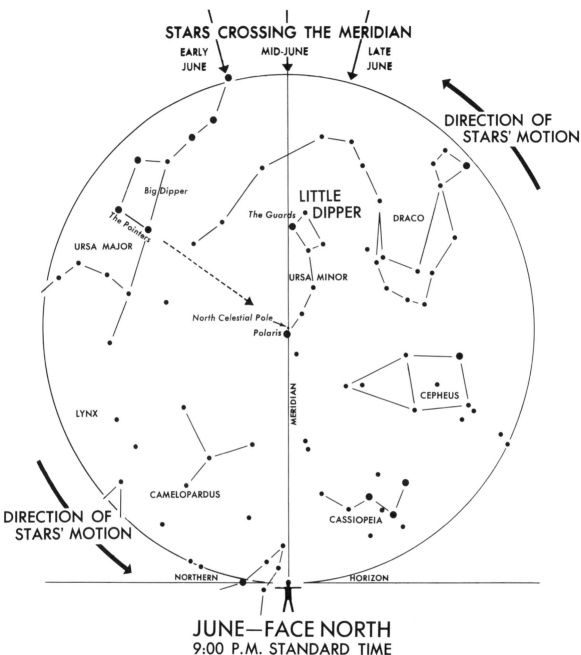

STARS CROSSING THE MERIDIAN

EARLY JUNE   MID-JUNE   LATE JUNE

DIRECTION OF STARS' MOTION

Big Dipper

LITTLE DIPPER

The Guards

DRACO

The Pointers

URSA MAJOR

URSA MINOR

North Celestial Pole

Polaris

CEPHEUS

MERIDIAN

LYNX

CAMELOPARDUS

DIRECTION OF STARS' MOTION

CASSIOPEIA

NORTHERN   HORIZON

JUNE—FACE NORTH
9:00 P.M. STANDARD TIME
10:00 P.M. DAYLIGHT SAVING TIME

The Little Dipper will be in a good position for viewing this month. Like the Big Dipper, it has three stars in its handle and four in its bowl. Most of the stars are faint, but having located Polaris by using the Pointers, you can easily find

46

the two bright stars in the bowl of the Little Dipper. These are called the Guards or the Guardians of the Pole because they are in a position to keep watch over the north celestial pole.

Probably the resemblance of this figure to the Big Dipper resulted in its being named Ursa Minor, the Little Bear. Like the Great Bear, the little one has an impossibly long tail represented by the dipper handle. Some nice efforts have been made to explain away this strange feature. It has been noted that while he hangs by his tail from the pole of the sky, he is constantly swung around in a circle. Perhaps his tail stretched under such a great strain.

Draco, the Dragon, is a wandering constellation that is most easily traced backward from tail to head. He has little competition in this part of the sky but can sometimes add confusion. You are likely to find that he is continually in the way when you are hunting for other constellations. But once you are acquainted with his long twisting shape, he will be more of a help than an obstacle in separating the other figures. Draco will be explored further in July.

47

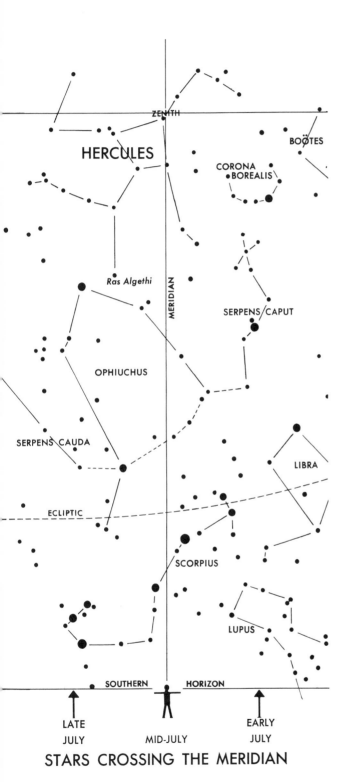

ZENITH

BOÖTES

HERCULES

CORONA
BOREALIS

MERIDIAN

Ras Algethi

SERPENS/CAPUT

OPHIUCHUS

LIBRA

SERPENS\CAUDA

ECLIPTIC

SCORPIUS

LUPUS

SOUTHERN   HORIZON

LATE
JULY   EARLY
      MID-JULY   JULY

STARS CROSSING THE MERIDIAN

JULY—FACE SOUTH
9:00 P.M. STANDARD TIME
10:00 P.M. DAYLIGHT SAVING TIME

JULY

You may have difficulty in locating Hercules, the Giant, but take your time and look for the most prominent part of the figure, called the Keystone. This is just northeast of Corona Borealis, which was explored in June. After mid-July this quadrangle is almost directly overhead, and once recognized, is easy to find again.

Despite his lack of bright stars Hercules is the superman of the summer sky. So many heroic feats have been attributed to him in legend that we cannot begin to list them here. Numerous other constellations have been woven into these stories, representing the weapons of Hercules and the monsters he defeated.

To picture our hero as he appears on most maps, you may want to face north and look at Hercules right-side up. (Either way, you are going to have to strain your neck a little to see this one.) You can make some order out of his sprawling arms and legs if you turn the chart upside down and imagine him kneeling on one knee with the other one bent. The narrow side of the Key-

48

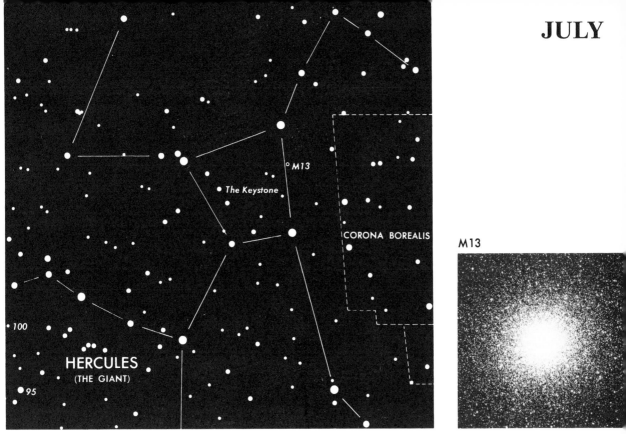

M13

stone is his belt. From the two fairly bright stars at his shoulders, one arm is extended and the other, holding a club, is upraised. The variable star with the Arabic name Ras Algethi marks his head. Though this star does not appear on the chart above, it is marked on the key chart at left.

Looking south again, concentrate on a spot one third of the way down the right-hand side of the Keystone. The smoky patch is M13, a beautiful globular star cluster. Binoculars will show you the cluster more clearly, and through a fair-sized telescope M13 is really a remarkable sight. It is estimated that there are more than 100,000 stars in the cluster. The photograph above, taken with the 200-inch Hale telescope, makes this believable.

If you have binoculars, spend some time searching through Hercules with them. There are some nice double stars in a rainbow of colors. For a start, try separating the two pairs marked 95 and 100 on the chart. The lower one has been glowingly described as apple green and cherry red in color.

Below Hercules is Ophiuchus (off i yoo' kus), the Serpent Bearer. He also is a giant, but hardly enjoys the same notoriety as Hercules.

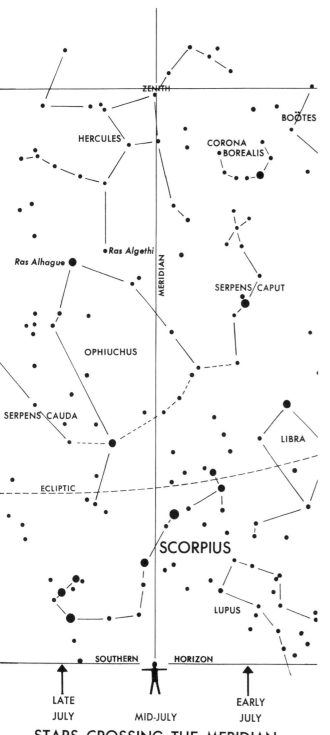

ZENITH

BOÖTES

HERCULES

CORONA
BOREALIS

Ras Algethi

MERIDIAN

Ras Alhague

SERPENS/CAPUT

OPHIUCHUS

SERPENS CAUDA

LIBRA

ECLIPTIC

SCORPIUS

LUPUS

SOUTHERN   HORIZON

LATE
JULY

MID-JULY

EARLY
JULY

STARS CROSSING THE MERIDIAN

JULY—FACE SOUTH
9:00 P.M. STANDARD TIME
10:00 P.M. DAYLIGHT SAVING TIME

Though they were seldom connected in legend, the two giants seem to be looking each other right in the eye.

In Greek legend Ophiuchus represents the father of medicine, with whom serpents were often associated. Imagine that Ras Alhague, the top star in the roof-shaped group at the upper end of the figure, is the head of Ophiuchus. The two stars to the east mark his right shoulder. Note the little group of four stars near this point. The two stars to the west mark his left shoulder as he faces us. The rest of this huge, but faint figure is difficult to visualize because it seems to be entangled with Serpens, the serpent which the giant is holding.

The constellation of Serpens once included the southern part of Ophiuchus, but now it is usually divided into two parts: Serpens Caput, the Serpent's Head to the west, and Serpens Cauda, the Serpent's Tail to the east. On the June charts we saw his head almost reaching up to Corona Borealis, the Northern Crown. His tail continues over to the August charts. Connect the two by means of the dotted line in Ophiuchus.

Not satisfied with surrounding Ophiuchus with a reptile, the ancients placed a huge scorpion beneath him. This is the prominent zodiacal constellation Scorpius, the Scorpion, found on the ecliptic.

50

The Scorpion all but overpowers the surrounding figures with his bright stars, the most spectacular one being the flamboyant red Antares (an ta' rez). The Greek name for the red planet, Mars, was Ares, and Antares means "the rival of Mars." When Mars is seen on the ecliptic anywhere near Antares, the similarity between the two glowing red objects cannot be missed. But this similarity is only visual. In reality Mars is a planet smaller than the earth, whereas Antares is a huge star *several hundred million miles in diameter.*

One legend links Scorpius with Orion, the great hunter of the January sky. It is said that Orion died from the scorpion's sting on his heel. However, as they now stand in the sky, they seem to be a safe distance apart. The fact that Orion also has a giant red star makes one wonder if the two magnificent stars were responsible for these figures being connected in ancient mythology.

Two star clusters, M6 and M80, are marked on the chart. If you have a good southern view on a clear night, you can see them faintly. There is an easily visible double star in the tail of the scorpion. With binoculars you can find other good doubles and star clusters and a nice field of stars around the scorpion's head. And don't overlook Antares itself. As you watch its shimmering light near the horizon, you will understand why the Chinese called it the Fire Star.

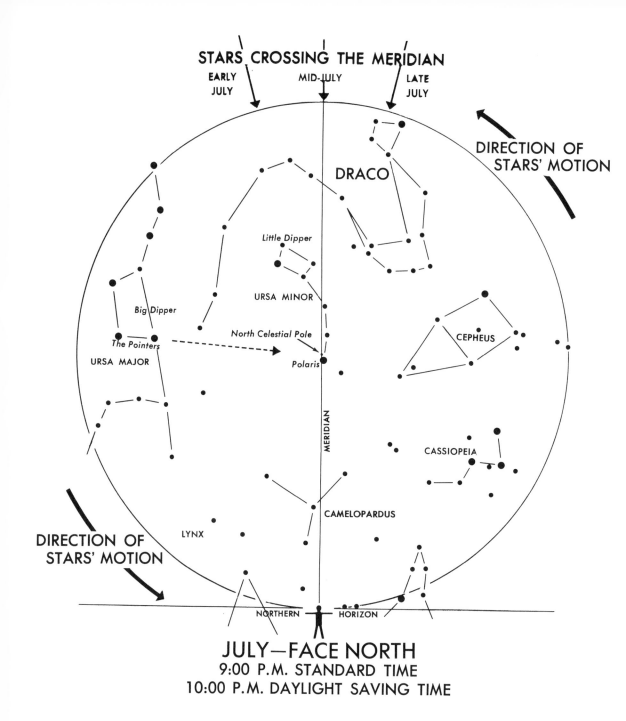

STARS CROSSING THE MERIDIAN

EARLY JULY   MID-JULY   LATE JULY

DIRECTION OF STARS' MOTION

DRACO

Little Dipper

URSA MINOR

Big Dipper

North Celestial Pole

The Pointers

URSA MAJOR

Polaris

MERIDIAN

CEPHEUS

CASSIOPEIA

DIRECTION OF STARS' MOTION

CAMELOPARDUS

LYNX

NORTHERN   HORIZON

JULY—FACE NORTH
9:00 P.M. STANDARD TIME
10:00 P.M. DAYLIGHT SAVING TIME

The Big Dipper, which is a part of Ursa Major, the Great Bear, is still prominent, though it is on its "downhill" journey in the northwest. Parts of Ursa Minor, the Little Bear, whom we met in June, are still on the meridian. (Polaris, of course, is always near it.) July is another good month to become well acquainted with this important little constellation.

52

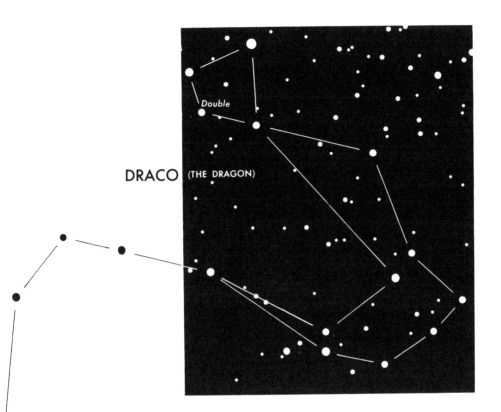

DRACO (THE DRAGON)

Arching over Ursa Minor is the curving figure of Draco, the Dragon. As we mentioned in June, it seems easiest to follow Draco's winding pattern if you begin with his tail, a little to the west and between the two dippers. Late this month you will see the distinctive quadrangle of his head almost directly above you. Then by studying the chart, you can find the double curve connecting his head to his tail.

There is an exceptional double star marked in Draco's head. When divided with binoculars, the stars are nearly alike in size and both a lovely icy blue color.

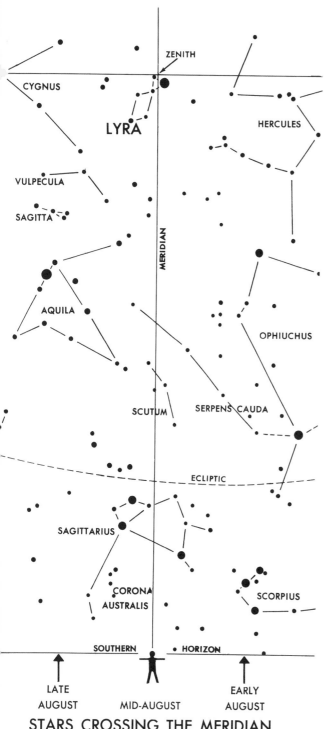

ZENITH

CYGNUS

LYRA

HERCULES

VULPECULA

SAGITTA

MERIDIAN

AQUILA

OPHIUCHUS

SCUTUM

SERPENS CAUDA

ECLIPTIC

SAGITTARIUS

CORONA
AUSTRALIS

SCORPIUS

SOUTHERN · HORIZON

LATE
AUGUST   MID-AUGUST   EARLY
AUGUST

STARS CROSSING THE MERIDIAN

AUGUST—FACE SOUTH
9:00 P.M. STANDARD TIME
10:00 P.M. DAYLIGHT SAVING TIME

AUGUST

Look overhead in the middle of August into the cold blue-white brilliance of Vega (vee′ ga), the brightest star in the summer sky. Near it are five fairly dim stars, rather like chips set beside a diamond. This group comprises the constellation of Lyra, the Lyre, or the Harp. At first the figure is elusive, but it comes into focus quite easily if you start with Vega and locate the small equal-sided triangle. Below this is a parallelogram which shares one star with the triangle. The upper stars in the parallelogram are both binocular doubles.

Concentrate on the top star in the triangle, and if your eye is keen, the star may look slightly elongated. Binoculars will separate it into a perfect pair of stars. But that isn't the end—a medium-sized telescope splits each of these stars into *another* perfect pair.

LYRA (THE HARP)

Double-
double

Vega

M 57   Sheliak

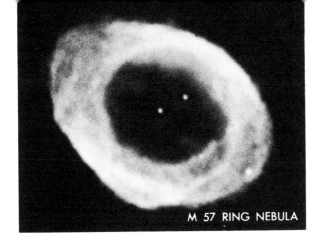

M 57 RING NEBULA

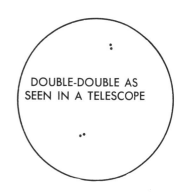

DOUBLE-DOUBLE AS SEEN IN A TELESCOPE

This is the well-known Double-double, an extraordinary sight.

When you study the two brighter stars at the bottom of Lyra, you are likely to notice that they do not have the same comparative brightness that is shown on the charts. This is because the star with the Arabic name of Sheliak is a variable. Because a great change in brightness can be observed in the short space of twelve or thirteen days, it is one of the most interesting variable stars to watch from night to night. It is sometimes brighter than the star to the left, and sometimes fainter.

A wonderful object in Lyra is the telescopic Ring Nebula, or M57. The photograph above was taken with the 200-inch Hale telescope and shows the nebula in good detail. However, it is almost more exciting when seen through an 8-inch telescope. It appears as a tiny but exquisite "smoke ring."

Cygnus, the Swan, and Aquila, the Eagle, will start over the meridian late in the month. They are interesting to look at now, but we will meet them in September when they are at their best.

Some acquaintances from July—Serpens Cauda, the Serpent's Tail, and part of Ophiuchus, the Serpent Bearer—are still near the meridian about halfway up from the horizon.

Just below Serpens is the barely noticeable figure of Scutum, the Shield. On a clear moonless night you can see a star cloud southeast of the top star in the constellation. This is a section of the Milky Way where stars are so dense that they literally look like a small cloud.

Following Scorpius along the ecliptic, and aiming an arrow at him, is the zodiacal constellation of Sagittarius, the Archer. He represents a centaur, the half man, half horse figure so popular in Greek legend. Connecting the stars in Sagit-

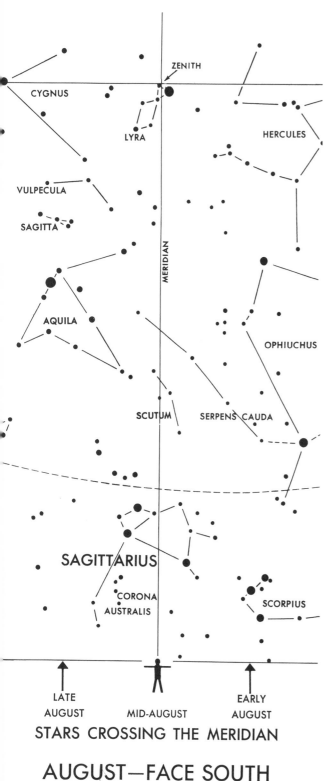

DIRECTION OF STARS' MOTION

ZENITH

CYGNUS

LYRA

HERCULES

VULPECULA

SAGITTA

MERIDIAN

AQUILA

OPHIUCHUS

SCUTUM

SERPENS CAUDA

SAGITTARIUS

CORONA
AUSTRALIS

SCORPIUS

LATE
AUGUST

MID-AUGUST

EARLY
AUGUST

STARS CROSSING THE MERIDIAN

AUGUST—FACE SOUTH
9:00 P.M. STANDARD TIME
10:00 P.M. DAYLIGHT SAVING TIME

tarius another way, the group forms quite a reasonable looking teakettle. Another name often used for part of this constellation is the Milk Dipper because the upside-down dipper seems to be reaching into the Milky Way.

This part of the sky around and above Sagittarius is fairly crowded with star clouds and nebulae. Spend some time hunting for "dust patches" here, with or without binoculars.

The faint curve of stars under the bowl of the Milk Dipper is Corona Australis, the Southern Crown.

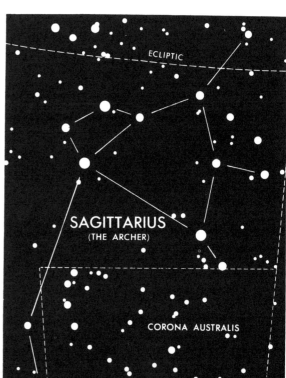

ECLIPTIC

SAGITTARIUS
(THE ARCHER)

CORONA AUSTRALIS

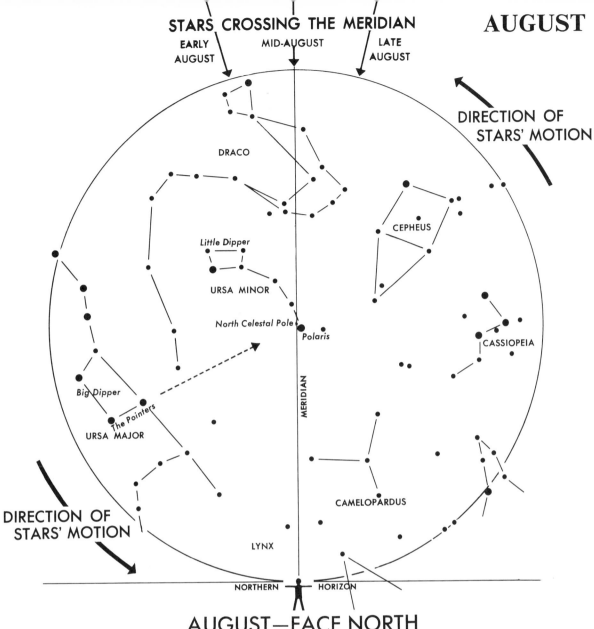

STARS CROSSING THE MERIDIAN

EARLY AUGUST   MID-AUGUST   LATE AUGUST

DIRECTION OF STARS' MOTION

DRACO

Little Dipper

URSA MINOR

North Celestal Pole

Polaris

CEPHEUS

CASSIOPEIA

MERIDIAN

Big Dipper

The Pointers

URSA MAJOR

CAMELOPARDUS

DIRECTION OF STARS' MOTION

LYNX

NORTHERN HORIZON

AUGUST—FACE NORTH
9:00 P.M. STANDARD TIME
10:00 P.M. DAYLIGHT SAVING TIME

Draco, the Dragon, will make his final appearance on the meridian during August, having been on stage for the past three months. The Big Dipper is almost directly to the west of the pole. And like a well-balanced seesaw, Cassiopeia, the Queen, reigns to the east. These three figures, along with Ursa Minor and Cepheus, comprise the five main north circumpolar star groups. This is the time of year to enjoy seeing them all together well above the northern horizon.

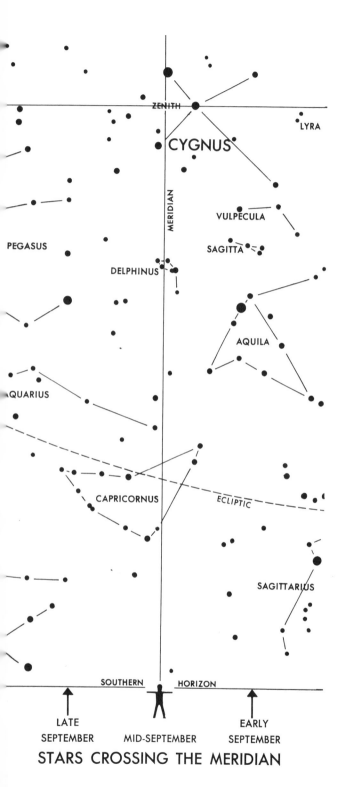

ZENITH

LYRA

CYGNUS

MERIDIAN

VULPECULA

PEGASUS

SAGITTA

DELPHINUS

AQUILA

AQUARIUS

CAPRICORNUS

ECLIPTIC

SAGITTARIUS

SOUTHERN   HORIZON

LATE
SEPTEMBER   MID-SEPTEMBER   EARLY
SEPTEMBER

STARS CROSSING THE MERIDIAN

SEPTEMBER—FACE SOUTH
9:00 P.M. STANDARD TIME
10:00 P.M. DAYLIGHT SAVING TIME

SEPTEMBER

The September sky is noted for two celestial birds. The impressive figures of the Swan and the Eagle will cross the meridian against the sparkling background of the Milky Way. Although he is not the first to cross, we will start with Cygnus, the Swan, because he is so easy to find.

Lyra, the Harp of the August sky, will now be to the west of the meridian, and Cygnus will be high overhead in the form of a nearly perfect cross. This part of the constellation is called the Northern Cross. Picture the Swan as flying southwest along the Milky Way, with Albireo marking his head and the bright Deneb at his tail.

Cygnus is connected with the Harp in legend. It was said that he represents Orpheus, who played the harp so beautifully that he charmed all the wild beasts in the forest. Even Pluto, the wicked god of the dark lower world, was so enchanted by the music that "iron tears" rolled down his cheeks. At his death Orpheus was changed into a swan and placed next to his ethereal harp in the sky.

58

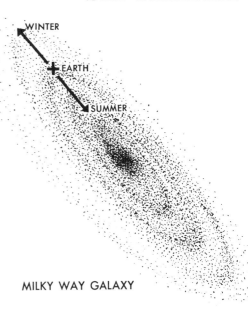

MILKY WAY GALAXY

It is difficult to find a main attraction in Cygnus because the whole field around this constellation is dazzling with double stars, beautifully colored stars, and star clusters. Searching the field with binoculars will turn up even more wonders. See if you can separate the double star Albireo, which is gold with a vivid blue companion. Note the variable star on the swan's neck. It is easily seen when at its brightest, but when the star fades, it cannot even be located with binoculars.

Near Deneb is what looks like a black hole in the sky. This marks the beginning of the rift in the Milky Way, an apparent separation which extends down over the southern horizon. The break is *not* due to the absence of stars, as we will see in a moment.

On these September evenings we have an opportunity to see the Milky Way in all its splendor. The brightest part of our galaxy arches across the sky in a silvery path. The stars are so numerous and distant that they seem to melt together into a glowing band of light.

As the earth makes its yearly trip around the sun, we see different parts of the Milky Way in different seasons. The diagram above shows why. On winter nights in the northern latitudes we are looking toward the outer edge of our galaxy. On late summer nights we can look in toward the center where the stars are more dense. They are so thick in some areas that through a telescope they look like

59

ZENITH

CYGNUS

LYRA

MERIDIAN

VULPECULA

PEGASUS

DELPHINUS

SAGITTA

AQUARIUS

AQUILA

CAPRICORNUS

ECLIPTIC

SAGITTARIUS

SOUTHERN   HORIZON

LATE
SEPTEMBER
MID-SEPTEMBER
EARLY
SEPTEMBER

STARS CROSSING THE MERIDIAN

SEPTEMBER—FACE SOUTH
9:00 P.M. STANDARD TIME
10:00 P.M. DAYLIGHT SAVING TIME

clouds. The wide-angle telescopic photograph on the opposite page shows some of these star clouds in one section of the Milky Way.

Besides stars (and probably countless planets) our Milky Way system contains masses of gas and dust, some of which form huge clouds, or nebulae. The nebulae that are most impressive to see are usually wispy and are illuminated by surrounding stars. Others may obstruct the light from the stars and appear as black holes or silhouettes. These areas, such as the one near Deneb, are sometimes called Coal Sacks. And the rift in the Milky Way? Great clouds of dust and gas between the earth and the stars have made a long valley of darkness blocking the starlight from our view.

South of Cygnus' head, straddling the dark rift, is Vulpecula, the Fox, which has no especially notable features. Next we come to Sagitta (sa jee′ ta), the Arrow, and Delphinus (del fye′ nus), the Dolphin, two constellations, which are small but are fairly easy to find because of their distinctive shapes. Sagitta is in the Milky Way and well worth exploring with binoculars. If you are adept at spelling names backward, you will see that two stars in Delphinus are named for Nicolaus Venator, an astronomer's assistant.

60

Aquila (ak′ wi lay), the Eagle, is flying northeast on the path of the Milky Way. One story says that Aquila belonged to Jupiter, the legendary ruler of the land. Jupiter had the power to hurl thunderbolts and flash lightning at will. When he wished to arm the heavens with these weapons, he chose the eagle, a high flyer, to carry the bolts skyward in his claws.

The white star Altair and its neighbors on either side, Tarazed and Alshain, make a very attractive trio. Note the variable star south of this group and compare it to the two nearby stars on the connecting line. Within a period of about seven days, you can watch it become as bright as the star to the left and as dim as the star to the right.

61

STAR CLOUDS IN THE MILKY WAY

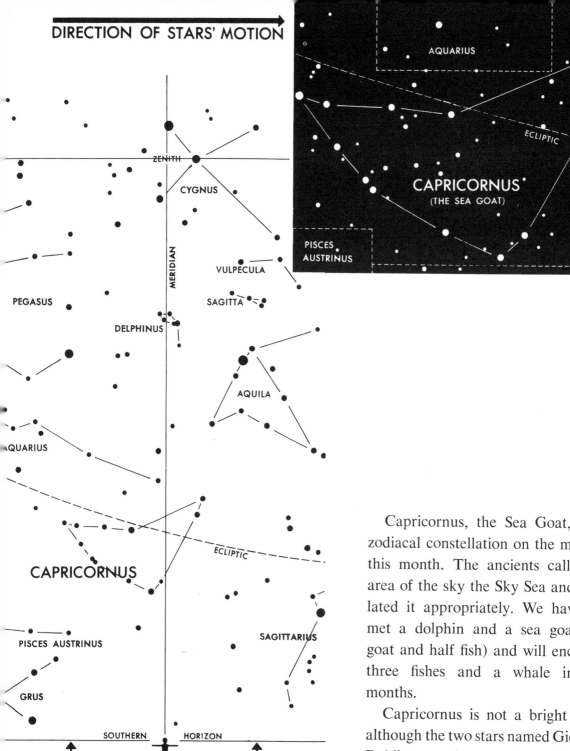

DIRECTION OF STARS' MOTION

AQUARIUS

Giec

Dabih

ECLIPTIC

ZENITH

CYGNUS

MERIDIAN

CAPRICORNUS
(THE SEA GOAT)

VULPECULA

SAGITTA

PEGASUS

PISCES
AUSTRINUS

DELPHINUS

AQUILA

AQUARIUS

ECLIPTIC

CAPRICORNUS

PISCES AUSTRINUS

SAGITTARIUS

GRUS

SOUTHERN   HORIZON

LATE
SEPTEMBER

MID-SEPTEMBER

EARLY
SEPTEMBER

STARS CROSSING THE MERIDIAN

SEPTEMBER—FACE SOUTH
9:00 P.M. STANDARD TIME
10:00 P.M. DAYLIGHT SAVING TIME

Capricornus, the Sea Goat, is the zodiacal constellation on the meridian this month. The ancients called one area of the sky the Sky Sea and populated it appropriately. We have now met a dolphin and a sea goat (half goat and half fish) and will encounter three fishes and a whale in later months.

Capricornus is not a bright figure, although the two stars named Giedi and Dabih are quite prominent. Both can be seen as double stars through binoculars, and Giedi can be separated without optics on a good clear night.

62

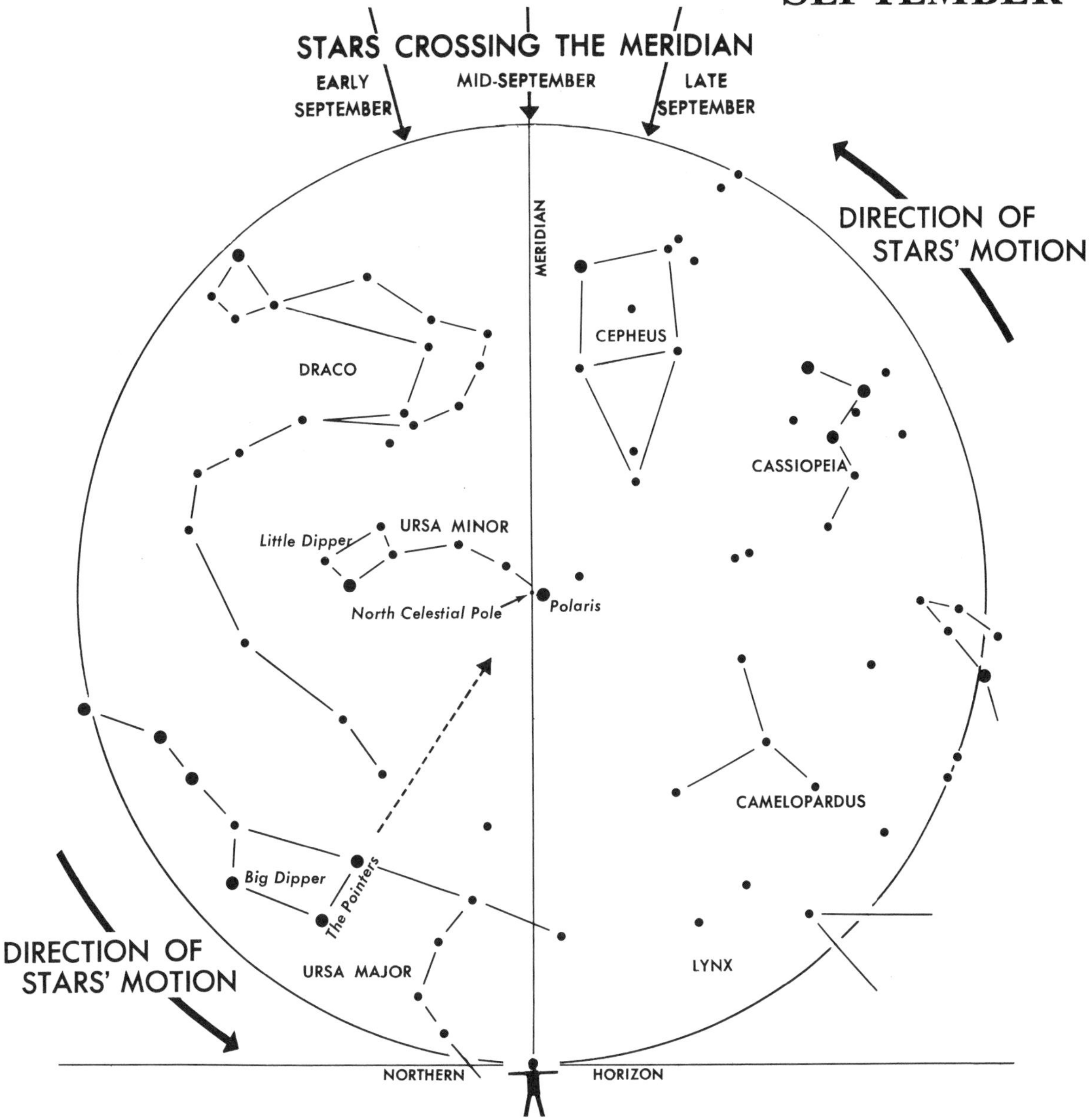

STARS CROSSING THE MERIDIAN

EARLY SEPTEMBER · MID-SEPTEMBER · LATE SEPTEMBER

DIRECTION OF STARS' MOTION

MERIDIAN

CEPHEUS

DRACO

CASSIOPEIA

URSA MINOR

Little Dipper

North Celestial Pole · Polaris

CAMELOPARDUS

DIRECTION OF STARS' MOTION

Big Dipper

The Pointers

URSA MAJOR

LYNX

NORTHERN HORIZON

SEPTEMBER—FACE NORTH
9:00 P.M. STANDARD TIME
10:00 P.M. DAYLIGHT SAVING TIME

As the Big Dipper sinks down toward the northwest, Draco follows it tail first—a dragon who doesn't look where he is going so much as where he has been. Cepheus the King and Cassiopeia the Queen are climbing "uphill." They will be explored as they cross the meridian in the coming two months.

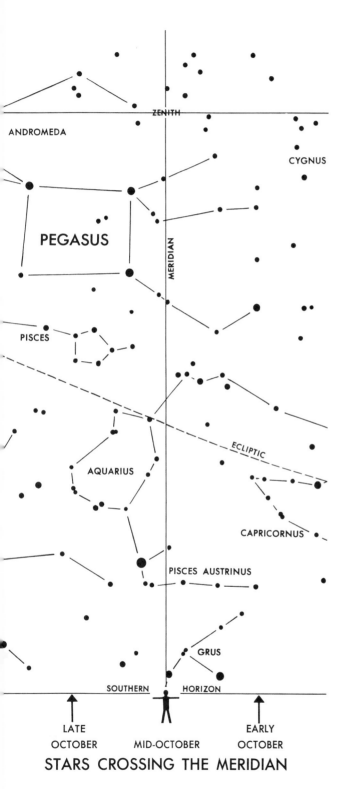

ZENITH

ANDROMEDA

CYGNUS

PEGASUS

MERIDIAN

PISCES

ECLIPTIC

AQUARIUS

CAPRICORNUS

PISCES AUSTRINUS

GRUS

SOUTHERN   HORIZON

LATE OCTOBER   MID-OCTOBER   EARLY OCTOBER

STARS CROSSING THE MERIDIAN

OCTOBER—FACE SOUTH
9:00 P.M. STANDARD TIME
10:00 P.M. DAYLIGHT SAVING TIME

OCTOBER

As the summer constellations move toward the west the Great Square of Pegasus, the Winged Horse, takes over a big dark stretch of the sky. It will be on the meridian or a little to the east of it throughout the month. The brightly marked square at first looks quite empty, but a little concentration will reveal many faint stars within its confines. A popular hobby among starwatchers is to see how many can be counted without optical help. Some claim to have spotted over fifty stars.

With a little imagination Pegasus can be pictured as a fairly credible horse, though only his front half is seen—and upside down at that. The Great Square represents his body. The line continuing from the lower right corner is his neck and head. His front legs are extended as he dashes through the heavens.

64

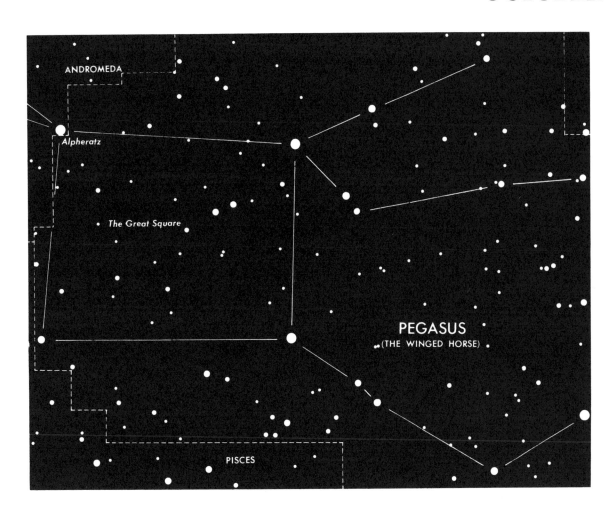

Pegasus was a marvelous creature who played a part in many legends. One of his owners was Aurora, the Goddess of Dawn, whose responsibility it was to put an end to night. Aurora rode the beautiful winged horse through the darkness to open the eastern gates of the sky for Apollo, the Sun God. Apollo then charged out of the east in his golden chariot and drove across the sky, carrying the blazing sun to the western horizon. If you wonder how Apollo and the sun got back to the east in time for the next day's appearance, they returned on the ocean in a golden boat or a winged cup.

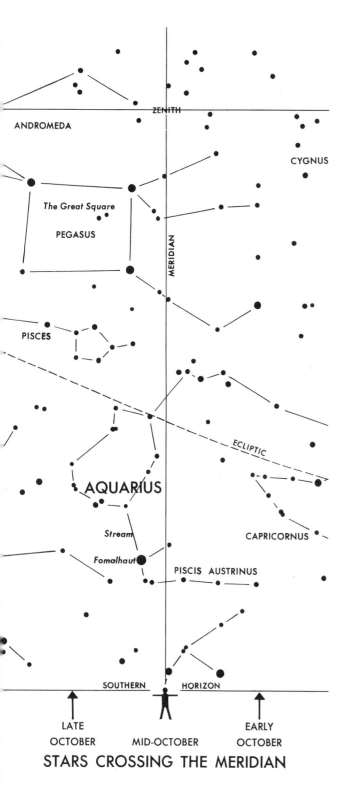

ANDROMEDA

ZENITH

CYGNUS

The Great Square

PEGASUS

MERIDIAN

PISCES

ECLIPTIC

AQUARIUS

Stream

CAPRICORNUS

Fomalhaut

PISCIS AUSTRINUS

SOUTHERN   HORIZON

LATE
OCTOBER   MID-OCTOBER   EARLY
OCTOBER

STARS CROSSING THE MERIDIAN

OCTOBER—FACE SOUTH
9:00 P.M. STANDARD TIME
10:00 P.M. DAYLIGHT SAVING TIME

South of Pegasus is Aquarius, the Water Carrier, a zodiacal figure on the ecliptic. The stars forming his over-turned water jar make a pretty group. Otherwise, the stars in this constellation are scattered and faint. The Arabs, however, seemed to hold some of them in high regard. For instance, note the stars Sadalmelik and Sadalsuud, both of which are supposed to signify good luck.

NGC 7009, the Saturn Nebula pictured opposite, is a well-known nebula in Aquarius even though it cannot be seen without a telescope. This is a good example of a *planetary nebula*, so named because their luminous disk-shapes were at one time thought to resemble planets.

Below Aquarius, in an area called the Sky Sea, is Piscis Austrinus, the Southern Fish. The star that marks his mouth is Fomalhaut (fom' al hote), the only bright star in this part of the sky. If you have trouble finding it, go back to the Great Square in Pegasus. The west side of the square points almost directly to it. On the old charts Aquarius is pictured pouring a stream of water from his jar into the fish's mouth. The path of the stream sparkles with faint double and triple stars which can be picked up with binoculars.

66

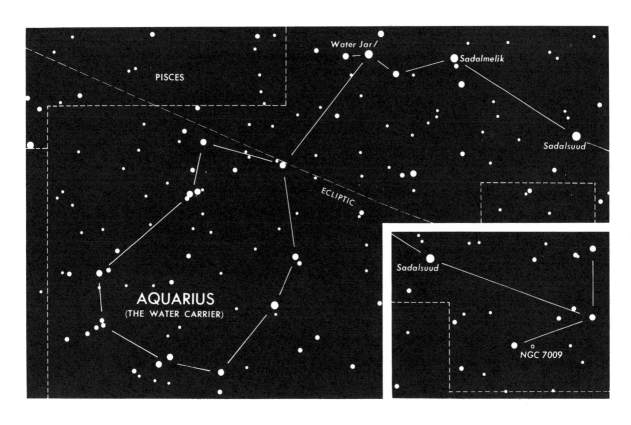

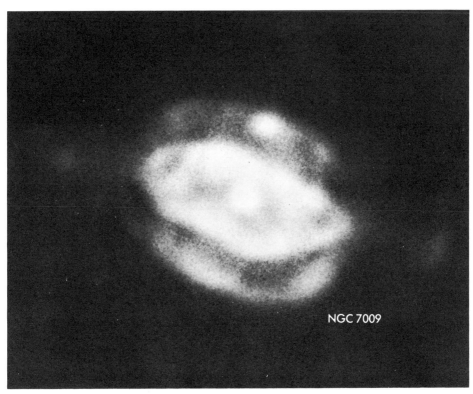

NGC 7009

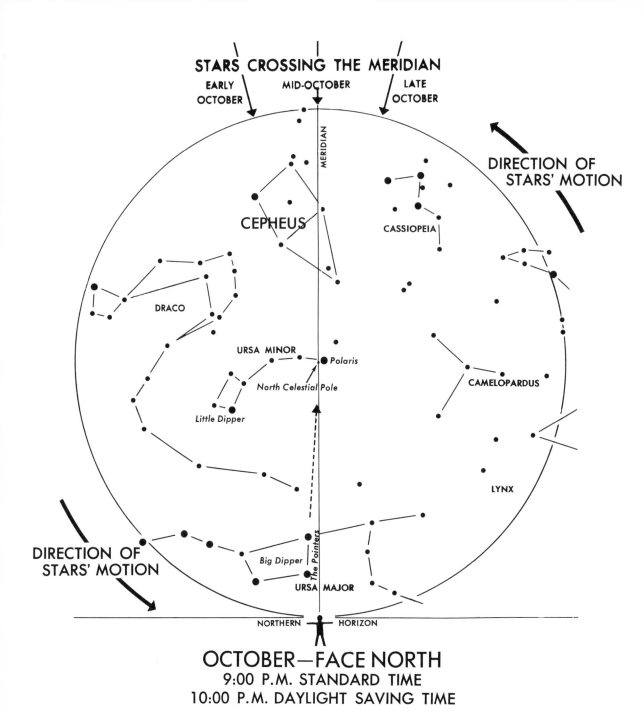

STARS CROSSING THE MERIDIAN

EARLY OCTOBER

MID-OCTOBER

LATE OCTOBER

DIRECTION OF STARS' MOTION

MERIDIAN

CEPHEUS

CASSIOPEIA

DRACO

URSA MINOR

Polaris

North Celestial Pole

CAMELOPARDUS

Little Dipper

LYNX

DIRECTION OF STARS' MOTION

Big Dipper

The Pointers

URSA MAJOR

NORTHERN ← HORIZON

OCTOBER—FACE NORTH
9:00 P.M. STANDARD TIME
10:00 P.M. DAYLIGHT SAVING TIME

The Big Dipper is now low on the northern horizon as Cepheus (see′ fe yus), the King, crosses the meridian high in the sky. Cepheus is less brilliant than his queen, Cassiopeia, who is just to the east. Nevertheless, he is one of the oldest and best known of the constellations. Cepheus is connected in legend to many of the figures to be seen while facing south in the coming months. Among these are

68

Perseus, the hero of December, and Andromeda, the princess of the November sky.

Cepheus is easily found because of his geometric pattern, a quadrangle the base of which forms one side of a triangle. Or he might be likened to a crooked house with a high peaked roof, seen upside down.

The variable star shown on the chart is quite a famous one and needs no optics

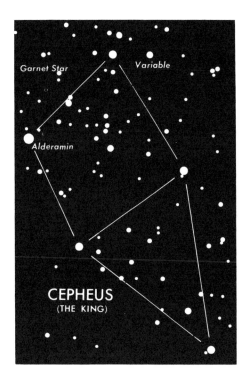

to be observed. It forms a triangle with two neighboring stars which make a good scale for comparing the brightness of the variable. (If the variable star is at its minimum, the triangle may be more clearly visible on the key chart at left than it will be in the sky.) In a period of about five and a half days, you can watch the light from the variable fluctuate from the intensity of the brighter star to that of the dimmer one and back again. The reason for this is probably that the star is steadily expanding and contracting. Binoculars will show that this star is also a double— yellow with a dimmer blue companion.

Note the faint but colorful Garnet Star. You will be especially struck by its deep red hue when you compare it with the white star Alderamin, located nearby.

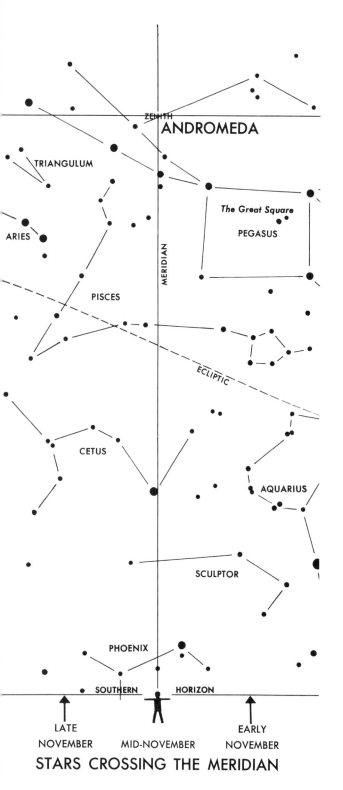

ZENITH
ANDROMEDA
TRIANGULUM
The Great Square
PEGASUS
ARIES
MERIDIAN
PISCES
ECLIPTIC
CETUS
AQUARIUS
SCULPTOR
PHOENIX
SOUTHERN   HORIZON

LATE
NOVEMBER   MID-NOVEMBER   EARLY
NOVEMBER

STARS CROSSING THE MERIDIAN

NOVEMBER—FACE SOUTH
9:00 P.M. STANDARD TIME

NOVEMBER

The feature attraction of the November sky is in the constellation of Andromeda (an drom' e da), the Princess. Here we find the galaxy M31, which is probably the most interesting wonder of the night sky. We will return to M31 after a look at the whole constellation.

Andromeda has one star in the Great Square of Pegasus, which was observed in October. This star has the Arabic name of Alpheratz. Three more fairly bright stars extend in a line from Alpheratz and almost seem to be reflected in the three dim stars strung out above them.

One of the oldest and most famous of the Greek legends involves several constellations in this part of the sky. Knowing the story will help you to remember the constellation figures. The cast includes two figures seen on the northern charts—Cepheus, the King (October), and Cassiopeia, the Queen (this month). Also included are Cetus, the Whale (this month), and Perseus, the Hero (December). However, as Andromeda is the heroine, the story might best be outlined here.

70

Cepheus was the king of Ethiopia. His wife, Queen Cassiopeia, was so boastful that she sat by the seashore, daring the sea nymphs to challenge her superior beauty. Enraged by her vanity, Neptune, the God of the Sea, caused great storms and floods to destroy the people. The king and queen were told that the only way to stop the destruction was to sacrifice their daughter Andromeda to Cetus, the terrible sea monster. Cepheus took the princess to the shore and sadly chained her wrists and ankles to a rock. The horrified population watched from a nearby cliff as the monster swam toward her.

Suddenly Perseus swooped down on winged feet. A great cheer arose as he fearlessly slew the monster and rescued Andromeda. Perseus won the everlasting admiration of the people and eventually married the princess.

M31 in Andromeda is the only galaxy in the northern sky that can be seen without optical aid. But viewed through binoculars or a telescope it is an unforgettable sight. The chart below shows the location of the galaxy.

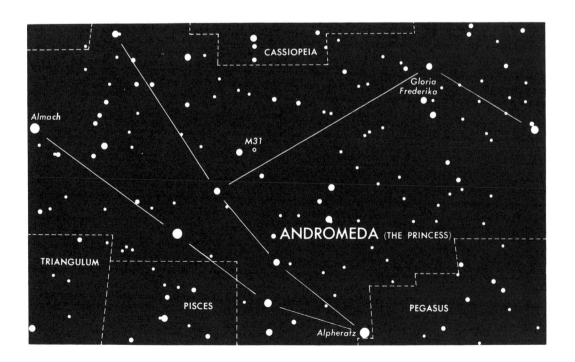

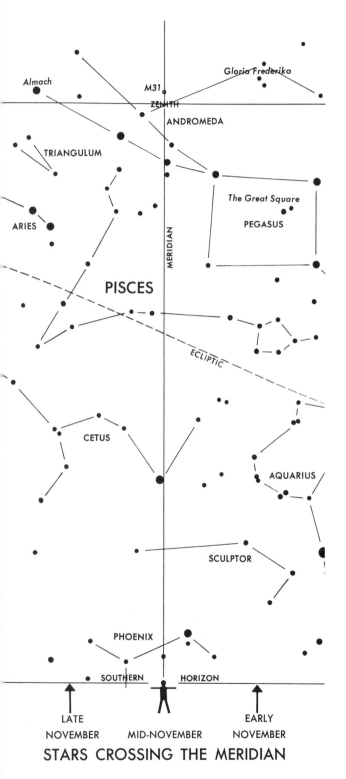

Almach

Gloria Frederika

M31
ZENITH
ANDROMEDA

TRIANGULUM

The Great Square

PEGASUS

ARIES

MERIDIAN

PISCES

ECLIPTIC

CETUS

AQUARIUS

SCULPTOR

PHOENIX

SOUTHERN   HORIZON

LATE
NOVEMBER   MID-NOVEMBER   EARLY
NOVEMBER

STARS CROSSING THE MERIDIAN

NOVEMBER—FACE SOUTH
9:00 P.M. STANDARD TIME

With the development of today's big telescopes, much has been learned about M31, the star system that was long ago described as the Little Cloud. Though somewhat bigger, it is very much like our own galaxy. It is approximately the same shape and contains millions of stars, light and dark nebulae, novae, variable stars, star clusters, and, very likely, planetary systems. The photograph of the Andromeda Galaxy opposite will give you some idea of what our Milky Way must look like from far out in space.

Perhaps less exciting, but well worth looking at with binoculars, is the orange star named Almach, which marks Andromeda's foot. This is actually a triple star, but you will be doing well to find one companion, a blue star.

While the tale of Andromeda is still fresh in mind, it might be a good idea to skip over Pisces for the moment and locate Cetus (see' tus), the Whale, farther south. The sky is uncluttered in this area and the curve of his back can be easily found. The rest of him will be explored in December. It is interesting to note that legend painted Cetus as a terrifying, scaly sea monster, but somewhere along the line he seems to have been converted into a whale.

Cetus inhabits the domain called the Sky Sea in ancient times. Between Cetus and Andromeda are two more sea creatures called Pisces (pi' seez), the

72

M31 ANDROMEDA GALAXY

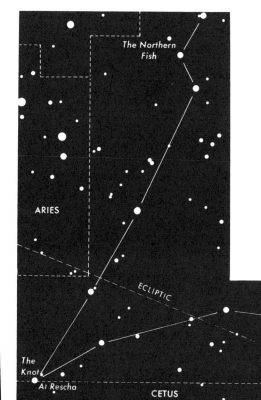

Fishes. This is a faint zodiacal constellation on the ecliptic that should be reserved for viewing on a very clear night. A good place to start is with the group of stars called the Circlet, located south of the Great Square of Pegasus. This represents the Western Fish. From here a fine stream of stars runs eastward and then northwest, where we find the Northern Fish near Andromeda. The stream of stars is pictured as a ribbon tied to the tails of the two fishes and knotted in the middle. The pale green star Al Rescha marks the knot.

Phoenix, the Bird, is far down on the southern horizon, out of sight to most people in the northern latitudes.

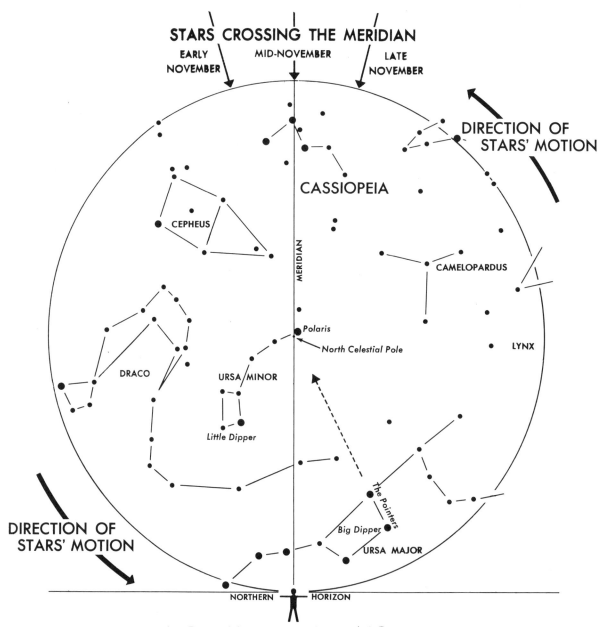

STARS CROSSING THE MERIDIAN

EARLY NOVEMBER   MID-NOVEMBER   LATE NOVEMBER

DIRECTION OF STARS' MOTION

CASSIOPEIA

CEPHEUS

MERIDIAN

CAMELOPARDUS

Polaris
North Celestial Pole

LYNX

DRACO

URSA MINOR

Little Dipper

The Pointers

Big Dipper

URSA MAJOR

DIRECTION OF STARS' MOTION

NORTHERN   HORIZON

NOVEMBER—FACE NORTH
9:00 P.M. STANDARD TIME

As the princess Andromeda dominates the sky to the south this month, her mother, Cassiopeia (kas i oh pee' a), the Queen, rules the meridian to the north. Her five bright stars take the shape of a spread-out M and in pictures usually represent a chair or throne. As this constellation reaches its highest point in the sky, the Big Dipper directly opposite is grazing the northern horizon with its handle.

One of the most exciting phenomena in the heavens took place in Cassiopeia in the year 1572. An exploding star, called a nova, appeared in the area marked

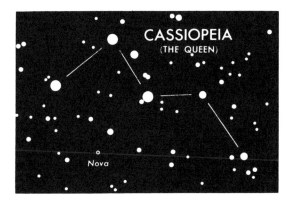

on the chart. It grew to a brilliance surpassing that of the planet Venus and could even be seen in daylight. In 1574 it faded out of sight, leaving behind a mystery concerning exactly what had happened to the star. This nova is called Tycho Brahe's star in honor of the famous astronomer who first observed and recorded it.

The field in and around Cassiopeia is rich in star clusters and double stars. If you have binoculars, you can find some beautiful objects that are out of sight for the eye alone.

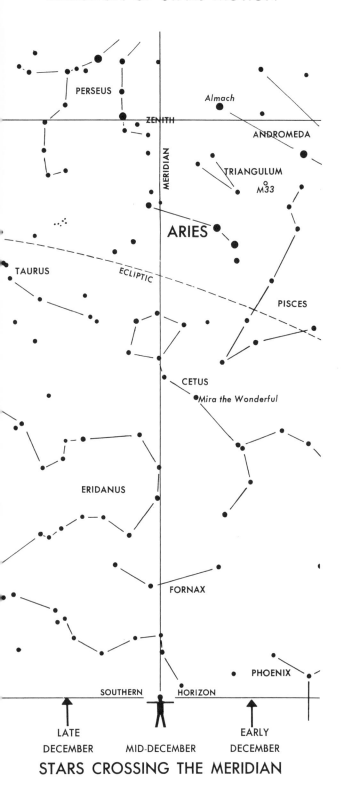

PERSEUS

Almach

ZENITH

ANDROMEDA

MERIDIAN

TRIANGULUM
M33

ARIES

TAURUS   ECLIPTIC

PISCES

CETUS

Mira the Wonderful

ERIDANUS

FORNAX

PHOENIX

SOUTHERN   HORIZON

LATE
DECEMBER   MID-DECEMBER   EARLY
                                DECEMBER

STARS CROSSING THE MERIDIAN

DECEMBER—FACE SOUTH
9:00 P.M. STANDARD TIME

DECEMBER

The long nights of December provide some extra latitude for star-watching. By going outdoors a few hours early, you can catch the late October and the November constellations on the meridian. And if you want to stay out late or just look to the east of the meridian at nine o'clock, you can get a preview of the exciting things to come in January. Perseus is the main attraction in the December sky, but we will save him for later because he crosses the meridian later in the month.

Below the star in Andromeda called Almach is a trio of stars named Triangulum, the Triangle. If you have high-powered binoculars and the night is clear, look for M33, which is marked on the key chart. This, like M31 in Andromeda, is a well-known spiral galaxy and relatively close to our own Milky Way Galaxy. M33 is a beautiful sight in telescopic photographs, as you can see on the right. This picture was taken with a 60-inch telescope.

South of Triangulum and following Pisces along the ecliptic is the zodiacal figure of Aries (ay' ri ez), the Ram. He is marked by three fairly bright stars

76

M33

but otherwise is not very imposing. Aries is connected in a popular legend to a group of southern constellations representing parts of the great ship Argo, which is mentioned in March. Aries is identified as the ram with the golden fleece that Jason and other Greek heroes sought on their daring expedition on the Argo.

The head of Cetus, the Whale, forms a rough circle to the south of Aries. Below this, on the whale's neck, is an amazing giant red star called Mira the Wonderful. This star is 300 times bigger than our sun in diameter and is a long-period variable star. Mira is some-

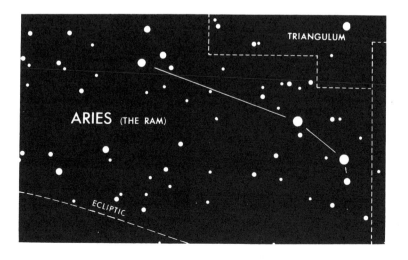

DIRECTION OF STARS' MOTION

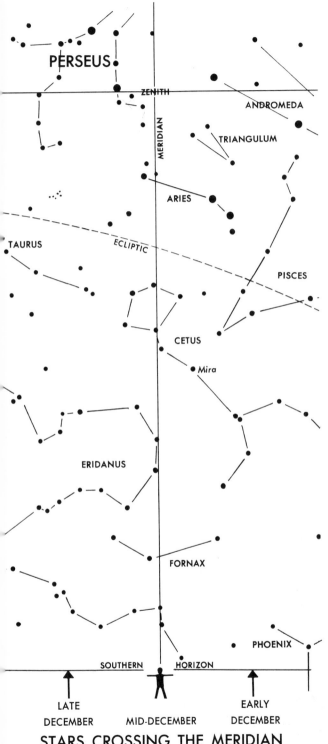

PERSEUS

ZENITH

ANDROMEDA

MERIDIAN

TRIANGULUM

ARIES

TAURUS

ECLIPTIC

PISCES

CETUS

Mira

ERIDANUS

FORNAX

PHOENIX

SOUTHERN   HORIZON

LATE DECEMBER   MID-DECEMBER   EARLY DECEMBER

STARS CROSSING THE MERIDIAN

DECEMBER—FACE SOUTH
9:00 P.M. STANDARD TIME

times brighter than any other star in the vicinity, and at other times cannot be found even with binoculars. Many of the well-known variables have been studied to a point where their activities can be predicted like clockwork. But in Mira's case neither the brightness nor the time period between maximum and minimum can be accurately determined. If you are lucky enough to find this star when it is fairly bright, check on it often—it offers a good opportunity to watch a variable in action.

Perseus (per' se us), the Hero, will be high overhead after mid-December. As this figure has no distinctive shape, you will probably find it by locating its two brightest stars, Mirfak and Algol.

In Greek legend Perseus was the adventurer who rescued Princess Andromeda from a terrible sea monster (see November). Another of his valorous deeds involved the worst monster of them all, the Gorgon Medusa. Medusa had hair made of snakes, huge eaglelike wings, and fiery eyes that turned any beholder into stone.

Perseus was given the awesome task of collecting Medusa's head as a token of his allegiance to the king. As he set off in search of the monster, the gods came to his aid. They gave him wings for his heels, a huge diamond sword, and a glittering shield. The wings took

78

him to the far-off land of the dreaded Medusa. He avoided the monster's devastating gaze by using the shield as a mirror to reflect her image, and with the sword he cut off her head. Then he took the loathsome head to the king, who is supposed to have been delighted with his present.

In the sky Perseus is usually pictured with his sword in one hand and the head of Medusa in the other. From her head glows Algol, the Demon Star. Algol can be observed to grow dim and then brighten again—because it is a short-period variable star.

It is a double star, having a larger, dimly lighted star revolving around a smaller, bright companion. Approximately every three days the fainter star passes between the brighter star and the earth. This spectacular eclipse reduces the light that we see from the earth to about one third of the normal brightness of the star.

Toward the south are the two constellations of Eridanus and Fornax. Eridanus, the River, will be seen again in January. Fornax, the Furnace, is hardly notable but is comforting to think about on a cold winter night.

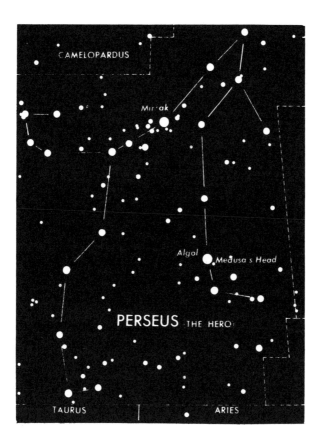

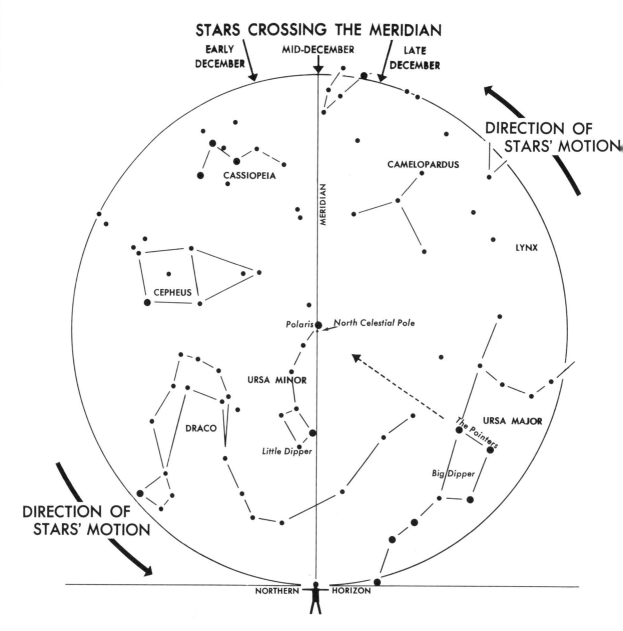

DECEMBER—FACE NORTH
9:00 P.M. STANDARD TIME

Cassiopeia, the Queen, of the November sky, has followed Cepheus, the King, across the meridian. A nearly empty area of the high northern sky approaches now, heralding the winter months.

The Big Dipper, led by the Pointers, is starting its slow climb upward, reminding us that the days will start to grow longer at the end of the month, and the Dipper will continue to rise higher as the new year progresses.

STARS ON THE MERIDIAN
BEFORE OR AFTER NINE O'CLOCK

The star charts for each month show the position of the stars on the meridian at about 9:00 P.M. Standard Time or 10:00 P.M. Daylight Saving Time. The table on the following two pages will help you find the chart which best shows what stars and constellations are on the meridian at an earlier or later hour.

STARS ON THE MERIDIAN
BEFORE OR AFTER NINE O'CLOCK

ST = Standard Time   DST = Daylight Saving Time

LATE JANUARY—EARLY FEBRUARY

ST	
6:00	MID-DECEMBER
7:00	EARLY JANUARY
8:00	MID-JANUARY
9:00	EARLY FEBRUARY
10:00	MID-FEBRUARY
11:00	EARLY MARCH
12:00	MID-MARCH

MID-FEBRUARY

ST	
6:00	EARLY JANUARY
7:00	MID-JANUARY
8:00	EARLY FEBRUARY
9:00	MID-FEBRUARY
10:00	EARLY MARCH
11:00	MID-MARCH
12:00	EARLY APRIL

LATE FEBRUARY—EARLY MARCH

ST	
6:00	MID-JANUARY
7:00	EARLY FEBRUARY
8:00	MID-FEBRUARY
9:00	EARLY MARCH
10:00	MID-MARCH
11:00	EARLY APRIL
12:00	MID-APRIL

MID-MARCH

ST	
6:00	EARLY FEBRUARY
7:00	MID-FEBRUARY
8:00	EARLY MARCH
9:00	MID-MARCH
10:00	EARLY APRIL
11:00	MID-APRIL
12:00	EARLY MAY

LATE MARCH—EARLY APRIL

ST	DST	
6:00	7:00	MID-FEBRUARY
7:00	8:00	EARLY MARCH
8:00	9:00	MID-MARCH
9:00	10:00	EARLY APRIL
10:00	11:00	MID-APRIL
11:00	12:00	EARLY MAY
12:00	1 A.M.	MID-MAY

MID-APRIL

ST	DST	
6:00	7:00	EARLY MARCH
7:00	8:00	MID-MARCH
8:00	9:00	EARLY APRIL
9:00	10:00	MID-APRIL
10:00	11:00	EARLY MAY
11:00	12:00	MID-MAY
12:00	1 A.M.	EARLY JUNE

LATE APRIL—EARLY MAY

ST	DST	
8:00	9:00	MID-APRIL
9:00	10:00	EARLY MAY
10:00	11:00	MID-MAY
11:00	12:00	EARLY JUNE
12:00	1 A.M.	MID-JUNE

MID-MAY

ST	DST	
8:00	9:00	EARLY MAY
9:00	10:00	MID-MAY
10:00	11:00	EARLY JUNE
11:00	12:00	MID-JUNE
12:00	1 A.M.	EARLY JULY

LATE MAY—EARLY JUNE

ST	DST	
8:00	9:00	MID-MAY
9:00	10:00	EARLY JUNE
10:00	11:00	MID-JUNE
11:00	12:00	EARLY JULY
12:00	1 A.M.	MID-JULY

MID-JUNE

ST	DST	
8:00	9:00	EARLY JUNE
9:00	10:00	MID-JUNE
10:00	11:00	EARLY JULY
11:00	12:00	MID-JULY
12:00	1 A.M.	EARLY AUGUST

LATE JUNE—EARLY JULY

ST	DST	
8:00	9:00	MID-JUNE
9:00	10:00	EARLY JULY
10:00	11:00	MID-JULY
11:00	12:00	EARLY AUGUST
12:00	1 A.M.	MID-AUGUST

MID-JULY

ST	DST	
8:00	9:00	EARLY JULY
9:00	10:00	MID-JULY
10:00	11:00	EARLY AUGUST
11:00	12:00	MID-AUGUST
12:00	1 A.M.	EARLY SEPTEMBER

If you want to look at the stars early in the evening during the first week in March, look at the table under LATE FEBRUARY—EARLY MARCH. Opposite 7:00 is listed EARLY FEBRUARY.

Turn to the month of February. The arrow at the bottom right of the chart points to the stars crossing the meridian at seven o'clock in early March.

LATE JULY—EARLY AUGUST

ST	DST	
8:00	9:00	MID-JULY
9:00	10:00	EARLY AUGUST
10:00	11:00	MID-AUGUST
11:00	12:00	EARLY SEPTEMBER
12:00	1 A.M.	MID-SEPTEMBER

MID-AUGUST

ST	DST	
8:00	9:00	EARLY AUGUST
9:00	10:00	MID-AUGUST
10:00	11:00	EARLY SEPTEMBER
11:00	12:00	MID-SEPTEMBER
12:00	1 A.M.	EARLY OCTOBER

LATE AUGUST—EARLY SEPTEMBER

ST	DST	
8:00	9:00	MID-AUGUST
9:00	10:00	EARLY SEPTEMBER
10:00	11:00	MID-SEPTEMBER
11:00	12:00	EARLY OCTOBER
12:00	1 A.M.	MID-OCTOBER

MID-SEPTEMBER

ST	DST	
8:00	9:00	EARLY SEPTEMBER
9:00	10:00	MID-SEPTEMBER
10:00	11:00	EARLY OCTOBER
11:00	12:00	MID-OCTOBER
12:00	1 A.M.	EARLY NOVEMBER

LATE SEPTEMBER—EARLY OCTOBER

ST	DST	
8:00	9:00	MID-SEPTEMBER
9:00	10:00	EARLY OCTOBER
10:00	11:00	MID-OCTOBER
11:00	12:00	EARLY NOVEMBER
12:00	1 A.M.	MID-NOVEMBER

MID-OCTOBER

ST	DST	
8:00	9:00	EARLY OCTOBER
9:00	10:00	MID-OCTOBER
10:00	11:00	EARLY NOVEMBER
11:00	12:00	MID-NOVEMBER
12:00	1 A.M.	EARLY DECEMBER

LATE OCTOBER—EARLY NOVEMBER

ST	
6:00	MID-SEPTEMBER
7:00	EARLY OCTOBER
8:00	MID-OCTOBER
9:00	EARLY NOVEMBER
10:00	MID-NOVEMBER
11:00	EARLY DECEMBER
12:00	MID-DECEMBER

MID-NOVEMBER

ST	
6:00	EARLY OCTOBER
7:00	MID-OCTOBER
8:00	EARLY NOVEMBER
9:00	MID-NOVEMBER
10:00	EARLY DECEMBER
11:00	MID-DECEMBER
12:00	EARLY JANUARY

LATE NOVEMBER—EARLY DECEMBER

ST	
6:00	MID-OCTOBER
7:00	EARLY NOVEMBER
8:00	MID-NOVEMBER
9:00	EARLY DECEMBER
10:00	MID-DECEMBER
11:00	EARLY JANUARY
12:00	MID-JANUARY

MID-DECEMBER

ST	
6:00	EARLY NOVEMBER
7:00	MID-NOVEMBER
8:00	EARLY DECEMBER
9:00	MID-DECEMBER
10:00	EARLY JANUARY
11:00	MID-JANUARY
12:00	EARLY FEBRUARY

LATE DECEMBER—EARLY JANUARY

ST	
6:00	MID-NOVEMBER
7:00	EARLY DECEMBER
8:00	MID-DECEMBER
9:00	EARLY JANUARY
10:00	MID-JANUARY
11:00	EARLY FEBRUARY
12:00	MID-FEBRUARY

MID-JANUARY

ST	
6:00	EARLY DECEMBER
7:00	MID-DECEMBER
8:00	EARLY JANUARY
9:00	MID-JANUARY
10:00	EARLY FEBRUARY
11:00	MID-FEBRUARY
12:00	EARLY MARCH

GLOSSARY

Celestial Poles: Two points in the sky directly above the north and south poles of Earth. An imaginary extension of our north pole leads to the north celestial pole which is marked, very nearly, by Polaris.

Circumpolar Stars: Stars that seem to circle around the celestial pole and never set below the horizon. This is due to the turning of Earth and not actual star motion. The number of circumpolar stars visible depends on the latitude of the observer.

Double Stars: A true double star, or *binary system,* consists of two stars that revolve around each other or around a common center of gravity. But we also use the term for *optical doubles,* which as seen in our line of sight from Earth appear to be close together. Actually they may be separated by vast distances.

Galaxy: A galaxy can be generally defined as a huge system of stars, gas, dust, planets, and other interstellar matter. The system is held together by gravity and rotates around its own center. Of the millions of galaxies in space, only a few are visible to the eye alone. One of these is the beautiful M31 in Andromeda (November). M31, like our own Milky Way, is a spiral galaxy. The Milky Way, sometimes referred to as *The Galaxy,* is listed separately.

M, or Messier, Objects: In the eighteenth century a French astronomer named Charles Messier (me' syay) was at work searching the sky for comets. He was constantly distracted by fuzzy patches which were not comets, although he didn't know what they were. Messier compiled a catalog of 103 of these nuisances, listing them as "objects to avoid." We now know that they are some of the most impressive nebulae, galaxies, and star clusters in the sky. Messier's numbers, along with several other numbering systems, are still used on most star charts. For instance, M1, the first entry in the catalog, designates the Crab Nebula in the constellation of Taurus (January).

Milky Way: (Also see **Galaxy.**) The Milky Way is the name of one of the millions of known galaxies. The planet Earth and our star, the sun, are a part of it. From far out in space our galaxy could look like just another "dust patch," but because we are inside this stellar system, we see it as a silvery path across the sky (see September).

Nebulae: Clouds of dust and gas in space. A *bright nebula* such as the Great Nebula in Orion (January) is lighted by stars that are nearby, or actually in, the cloud. A *dark nebula* absorbs or obstructs the light from the stars and looks like a black hole. A good example of this is the Horsehead Nebula, also in Orion. Many objects which were once grouped under the general classification of nebulae are now known to be star clusters or galaxies.

NGC: Abbreviation for New General Catalog, a numbering system used in most star atlases, which lists about 8000 star clusters, nebulae, and galaxies.

Nova: A nova is a star that has exploded, or erupted, into great brilliance, only to grow dim again in an unpredictable period of time.

Stars: Hot gaseous bodies in space which, unlike planets, shine by their own light. Our sun is rather an average star in size, even though more than one hundred Earths would fit across its diameter. See the diagram of Betelgeuse (January) for a look at a really big star. The color of a star is related to its temperature—they range from blue-white (hottest) to red (coolest).

Star Cluster: A group of stars moving through space together. *Open clusters* are loosely scattered stars such as the Hyades and the Pleiades in Taurus (January). A *globular cluster* is a more dense, or tightly packed, group of stars such as the great M13 in Hercules (July).

Telescopic Objects and Photographs: The purpose here is not to define telescopes, but to clarify references to them in this book. The size of a telescope means the diameter of the main lens or mirror. A small amateur's telescope could be one with a diameter of about 3 to 8 inches, although the tube itself would be several feet long.

In the last century the rapid development of photographic techniques has revolutionized the science of astronomy. The big observatory instruments such as the 200-inch Hale telescope are used almost exclusively to make long-exposure photographs of the wonders of the sky, some of which are reproduced in this book.

Variable Stars: Stars that do not shine with uniform brightness. The cause of this variation is not fully understood, except in the case of the *eclipsing variable*. This is simply a binary system, in which a darker star passes in front of a brighter one and cuts out some of its light. Algol, the Demon Star of December, is a fine example of this type of variable. Other variable stars seem to pulsate. That is, their gases expand and contract, causing a variation in light. The time cycle of a variable, from maximum brightness to minimum and back again, can be a period of a few days *(short period)* or several hundred days *(long period)*. Though many variables are highly predictable, some seem to flare up and fade with no consistency at all.

Watching a variable in action is an interesting pastime. But for those with even small telescopes, variable star observing can also be most useful. The American Association of Variable Star Observers (AAVSO) records observations sent in by amateur members from all countries. Their combined findings are then made available to astronomers and observatories all over the world. Your nearest planetarium can supply further information.

Zodiacal Constellations: The figures that lie in a zone along the line of the ecliptic. Although many of these constellations are dim, they are well-known because of their importance among the ancients, who believed that these stars controlled human destiny.